Hope Renew

MW00614722

Living things cannot be wholly pressed into a rational, scientific box. Categorizing and labeling are foreign to any living thing. This is just as true of plants as it is of people. Every living thing has its own subtle beauty and inherent strengths.

Writing any book requires that the material be organized for presentation in an orderly fashion. Although, in these pages, I categorize, label, dissect, and organize the medicinal properties of the various plants, please remember the following:

First: My husband and I (he does this better than I do) look at the plants—every one, and perhaps the rocks and minerals, too—as personal messages from a loving Heavenly Father. Because He understood that we would not always ask for, or even recognize His help in our lives, He endowed the various plants with His own healing capacities and invited us to partake of them to balance and heal our own lives. Plants affect us, not just on a physical (vitamin and molecular) level, but on a spiritual plane as well. It is impossible to use an herbal remedy to heal the physical body without partaking of its ability to bring light and wisdom, healing and peace into your life. The peace and wisdom will be multiplied many times over if you use the herbs with thanksgiving to the Creator and an acknowledgement of the role of the atonement in the healing of both physical and emotional (spiritual) pain.

Secondly: Plants are living things. To feel the living spirit and intelligence of each plant is the true foundation of herbal medicine. Just as each plant can exemplify the attributes of our loving Father, so can the plants personify some lessons about the operation of the body and the soul. The possibilities for learning are endless. To think herbally is to think differently; we must think as nature does—holistically. Nature emphasizes the whole, rather than the precise piece, and nature has an inherent logic and wisdom.

In studying herbals, our goal is to appreciate the mysteries inherent in a human soul, and ascertain the best holistic approach to imbalances within that soul/body/mind complex.

In order to understand a medicinal herb, it is helpful to understand its use in an historical context. Unfortunately, much herbal knowledge has been lost and this continuity is not always possible. It is interesting to note that whether the use of a particular herb was by ancient folk doctors, allopathic medical personnel, homeopathic practitioners, etc., the medicinal properties claimed for the herb were always very similar. The medicinal properties of the herb do not change with time, methods of preparation, or the philosophy of the user. What works, works—even for the skeptical!

Herbs live in and adapt to enviornmental stresses which correspond in many ways to problems in our own lives. The excesses of climate they experience are much like the distressing life situations which we sometimes face. The triumphs of their life force over the adversities of nature become an integral part of their genetic makeup and healing properties. We can find strength and growth in our own lives and bodies through our experiences with God's creations. Herbs can be both our medicines and a reference point for understanding ourselves and the world around us. *Plants, by their very nature, act upon the imbalances within our systems, not on the viruses and bacteria which settle into these imbalances environments. They strengthen us against adversity and attack.*

Last, and to me, most important: I have found that herbs are many times more effective if used with gratitude, especially gratitude to a loving Creator who established this world in such a way that the things we need for balance and health, in every aspect of our lives, are everywhere around us. This need for gratitude has been brought home to me in a myriad of ways over the years. I don't believe that God requires our gratitude for His glory. The commandment to be grateful is an example of God explaining to us what is best for our own souls. If you don't do it already, try doing all that you do in this holistic medical world with a large measure of gratitude.

To move into the realm of healing with God's living pharmacy is to take a fuller measure of responsibility for ourselves, our welfare and happiness. The accepting of this responsibility, coupled with gratitude to the Creator, blesses and strengthens us in a myriad of ways.

May you find as much joy in the herbal journey as I have.

Butterfly Miracles
with
Herbal Remedies

LaRee Westover

butterflyexpressions.org
butterflymiracles@hotmail.com

ISBN-978-0-9818396-6-0

Revised December 2010

©Copyright Butterfly Expressions
LLC 2010

Legalese

There is absolutely no substitute for caution and common sense!

This herbal booklet is written for general information and education only. It is not my intent to diagnose or prescribe for any ailment whatsoever. Your use of the information contained in this book is entirely at your own discretion, and is also, entirely your own responsibility. My goal is, simply, to bring to your attention things that, when I became aware of them, seemed to make significant changes in the quality of my life. It is not meant to be training in psychology, psychotherapy, or medicine of any kind. You are advised to apply the techniques and information along with the assistance of competent professionals.

There are details concerning the safe use of plants as medicnal remedies that cannot be contained in any book. Before using an herbal preparation the reader is advised to seek the assistance of a competent professional.

The statements and products mentioned in this booklet have not been evaluated by the FDA. They reflect traditional and anecdotal usage and data from recent scientific studies.

I hope you come to love and appreciate the wonders of God's herbal pharmacy as much as I do!

Rev 12/10

Table of Contents

Recipes-continued

Section One
Herbal Medicines

Chapter One
Vitamins and Minerals

**Herbals are not meant to just to cure disease, although that is what we often resort to using them for.
They are meant to aid us in building healthy, resilient, well-balanced, drug-free bodies.
Ours is a positive healing science;
not merely the practice of putting out fires as they erupt in our lives.**

I have been using herbs and herbal remedies for 30 years. For most of that time I have been considered quite knowledgeable in the field, but I can honestly tell you that I never really met with much success, comparatively, until I learned to think in holistic terms. Holistic means, to me, that you look at the whole person and not just at the presenting symptoms or at the disease. Treating just the presenting symptoms is a band-aid approach at best, and rarely solves a problem for very long. Man is a spiritual, emotional, mental being, much more than just his physical body, and no true healing ever takes place without addressing the various layers of our existence. A good healer will learn to use other modalities (such as homeopathic remedies, essential oils, acupressure, etc.) in their quest for optimum and vibrant health.

This booklet is about herbal medicines, and as such, it will be concerned mostly with the physical aspect of our bodies. Herbs do, however, have frequencies and life energy just as essential oils do, but that will not be the major focus of this study. Here, we will address (a) how and why herbals work, (b) the different categories and effects that herbs can have on the body, and we will discuss (c) the different methods of preparation and administration that are commonly employed in their use. An effective healer will remember that in all that we do we are merely acting as an assistant to the body's own vital force and energy.

Herbal medicines are just potential, corrective foods, and these only become active as they are selected from the blood stream, absorbed into the bioplasm and converted by the Spiritual within into vital life energy.   (Dr. John R. Christopher)

The Medical Model

Below is a quote from the Reverend John Wesley (1703-1791) concerning the historical abandonment of herbs in medicine.

As theories increased, simple medicines were more and more disregarded and disused; till in a course of years the greater part of them were forgotten, at least in the more polished nations. In the room of these, abundance of new ones were introduced by reasoning, speculative men, and those more and more remote from common observation. Hence, rules for the application of them, and medical books, were immensely multiplied; till at length, physics became an abstruse science, quite out of the reach of ordinary men. Physicians now began to be held in admiration, as persons who were something more than human. And profit attended their employ, as well as honor, so that they had now two weighty reasons for keeping the bulk of mankind at a distance, that they might not pry in to the mysteries of their profession. To this end they increased those difficulties by design, which were in a manner by accident previously. They filled their writing with abundance of technical terms utterly unintelligible to plain men.

©**Copyright Butterfly Expressions, llc 2010   Butterfly Miracles with Herbal Remedies**

What is the difference between natural healing and orthodox medicine? These two approaches are miles apart in both theory and practice. Orthodox medicine would have you believe that the cure of disease lies in killing the offending germ or in removing the damaged body part. The natural healer, on the other hand, recognizes that disease is the result of the violation of the laws of nature. These violations need not be intentional to be harmful. The holistic method also recognizes that germs cannot exist in harmful numbers or for any length of time in or on healthy tissue.

The most effective way to cure disease is to aid the body in its own healing processes. We accomplish this by eliminating poisons and toxins using the body's eliminative channels. Good nutrition and the use of a few natural remedies soon returns the body to health and vitality.

Disease is not cured by feeding the body poisonous substances! In my opinion, <u>nothing should be added to the body in times of illness that cannot be used by the cells in their healing and rebuilding processes.</u> Herbal agents which kill invading organisms do so, for the most part, by strengthening the immune system and supporting cellular health and structure.

Dr. John R. Christopher (an experienced and effective therapist) believed that much of what we call disease is simply the body's own way of dealing with imbalances and deficiencies. In other words, the fever that is burning away and killing the invading germs is not the enemy. The fever may need watching and controlling but it should not be eliminated altogether until it has accomplished its work. Another example might be diarrhea caused by eating bad food or a food to which you are intolerant. Any remedy employed should aim at eliminating the foreign bacteria introduced by the food and strengthening the digestive system so that the food you are allergic to is no longer a problem.

Many other diseases are merely the manifestation of nutritional deficiencies. The body often uses pain as a way of getting our attention. If we are failing to give our body the nutrition it needs, it will surely find a way to let us know about it. This will be discussed more completely in Chapter 1 of this booklet.

A Basic Rule of Alternative Therapy: (I am sure we will discover a few more rules as we go along.)

There are no incurable diseases - only incurable people!

Incurable people fall into the following categories:
- a) People who will not follow the program outlined, or follow through with using what is needed on a regular basis.
- b) People who are not interested in thinking and learning and taking responsibility for themselves. It is almost impossible to know every symptom, every feeling, and every nuance of a person's health and accomplish as much good for them as they could accomplish for themselves by taking some responsibility and obtaining even a little bit of knowledge.
- b) People whose illness is feeding some emotional need or pattern, or people who are deriving some benefit from their illness. The asthma that is getting the child out of P.E. at school or the kidney that is constantly stressed because of unresolved fear or assertiveness issues might be examples of these emotional patterns.
- c) Someone whose "time has come." We are not supposed to live forever in this world, nor are we meant to be completely free of trials and troubles.
- d) A person who is not patient with the process. Healing, like life, is a journey. It probably took years to get the body into this mess. It may take months, maybe even years, to return it to good health. Meanwhile, the band-aid approach can make life more comfortable and enjoyable.

©**Copyright Butterfly Expressions, llc 2010   Butterfly Miracles with Herbal Remedies**

The Focus of Your Work

Herbal remedies and other natural modalities can be utilized in two differing ways. The first method is to focus on the immediate NOW! Someone you love is ill or unhappy today. Your concern becomes making the pain and distressing symptoms go away, and making them to go away RIGHT NOW! This approach accomplishes a great deal of good in people's lives. It becomes easy to assume that your work is done when the current crisis has passed.

With natural healing methods our focus is the building of healthy, disease free, stress resistant bodies and minds. We are looking for root causes and basic imbalances within ourselves. We are seeking ways to eliminate problem areas and become healthy, happy, vibrant versions of ourselves. We must, of course, cope with what is happening in our lives right now. We have to get up and function each day, after all, but at the same time we need to hold in our minds the goal of strong immune systems and healthy minds and bodies. Try not to lose sight of this goal amidst the stresses of every-day living. It is far better to eliminate the asthma completely than to get really good at coping with frequent attacks!

Vitamins and Minerals

Necessary for good health?

I doubt that anyone would disagree with me when I say that vitamins and minerals—combined with the right kinds of fats—are absolutely essential to healthy bodies and minds. Study after study has confirmed the connection of vitamins and minerals to health.

The lack of certain vitamins and minerals has also been lined to unhealthy (disease) states of the body and mind. Vitamins are powerful substances. We need only microscopic amounts of some of them in our diets to stay healthy. Take away those tiny quantities and our bodies soon run into deep metabolic trouble. The body responds, often very quickly, to improved nutrition. Nutritional deficiencies are easily preventable in this land of plenty.

How much is enough?

Most of us are familiar with the phrase "Recommended Dietary Allowance" (RDA) but what, exactly, does this phrase mean? Most orthodox nutritionists believe that if you are getting all the recommended nutrients in the recommended amounts, you are well on your way to being just fine. A growing number of scientists, doctors, and informed laymen disagree with this idea.

The RDA's are defined by the committee setting the standards as "the levels of intake of essential nutrients considered, in the judgement of the committee on Dietary Allowances of the Food and Nutrition Board on the basis of available scientific knowledge, to be adequate to meet the <u>known nutritional needs of practically all healthy persons</u>."

The RDA statement is a carefully worded statement which must be just as carefully interpreted.

Known nutritional needs?   The facts coming out of research about nutrition and its effect on health (and disease) change daily. The RDA's certainly do not reflect this growing body of research.

©**Copyright Butterfly Expressions, llc 2010   Butterfly Miracles with Herbal Remedies**

Practically all?

Some of us, for varying reasons, need more than other people do of certain nutrients, but the statement is based on the statistical probability that this amount will cover the needs of 97% of people. Perhaps a 3% risk does not seem great, until you consider that you are taking the same risk with each of the 40 or so nutrients being named. A mathematician would tell you that if you consume exactly the RDA for each essential nutrient, you have at least a 50-50 chance of becoming deficient in more than one of them.

Healthy persons?

The committee clearly points out that "these values do not take into account special needs for nutrients arising from such problems as. . . inherited metabolic disorders, infections, chronic disease, and the use of medications—which require special dietary and therapeutic measures."

The case could certainly be made that in this day and age of pollution and pills, healthy people are becoming an extinct species. ***The committee has merely set minimal requirements for minimal health.***

The following pages are based on information found in the book The Complete Book of Vitamins compiled by the authors of Prevention Magazine and published by Rodale Press, leaders in books on health, nutrition, and alternative medicine. I have also drawn on many other sources and on years of experience in herbal nutrition. It is impossible to say what your body's exact requirements for specific nutrients are, but the following pages may provide you with some basic guidelines.

Researchers, nutritionists, scientists, and nearly everyone else are constantly warning us about the bad effects of certain dietary habits on our health. The good news is that there have been major studies showing the *good* effects of eating the right kinds of foods also. One of these studies was conducted in Israel by Aviva Palgi, Ph.D. In this study she analyzed 28 years worth of data in order to determine the cumulative effects of dietary changes on specific disease mortality rates.

Among her findings was a report that indicated that in Israel, between 1949 and 1977, the death rate from heart attacks more than doubled while the death rates from high blood pressure, stroke, and peptic ulcer also increased significantly. During that same time period, according to carefully kept statistics, it was reported that the Israelis had changed their eating habits significantly. By the 1970's, they were consuming 52 percent more fat than in previous years. They had also decreased the amount of calories coming from complex carbohydrates, such as grains, while almost doubling their intake of simple carbohydrates, such as refined sugar.

What makes this study most useful is that Dr. Palgi not only looked at obvious dietary factors like fats and carbohydrates, but she also examined how the increased intake of specific vitamins and minerals directly affected those same diseases.

We will discuss briefly just a few of the basic vitamins and minerals that are the building blocks of optimum health. This should illustrate how beneficial good nutrition can be. I would highly recommend the book mentioned in the last paragraph of the previous page for some very interesting reading on this important subject.

Vitamin A

Dr. Palgi's study indicated, very strongly, that the more vitamin A individuals consumed, the less likely they were to suffer from heart disease, high blood pressure, stoke, and peptic ulcer. While some Israelis were eating more fats, others were enjoying lots of fruits, vegetables, and other foods that were high in vitamin A and other nutrients. And those who ate these good, natural foods stayed healthier than those who didn't.

©Copyright Butterfly Expressions, llc 2010   Butterfly Miracles with Herbal Remedies

The following is a quote from Dr. Palgi:

> Right now, we know that 5,000 international units of vitamin A daily is an absolute requirement for health. But for people in a pre-disease state, more may be needed. I know that in view of the results of my study I am more conscious of my diet, and I try to eat plenty of vitamin A-rich foods while also keeping my total fat intake as low as possible.

Some of the benefits you may expect from getting sufficient Vitamin A in your diet are: improved blood cholesterol levels, improved anti-oxidants in the blood, protection against cardiovascular diseases, improved resistance to illness, decreased likelihood of developing cancer, better respiratory health, better skin health, better recovery from accident, illness, or surgery, better vision—especially at dusk, improved bowel function, better dental health, and increased energy levels in the thymus gland.

Nutrition lists almost always show that liver has far more vitamin A than any other single food, and some scientists claim that the vitamin A in liver is more complete. However, it is certainly possible to get all the vitamin A that you need from plant sources in your daily diet. It is recommended by this study and others that you get between 8,000 and 20,000 I.U.s daily. This is 5 to 10 milligrams, if you prefer that scale.

The best food sources of vitamin A include liver - 3 ounces - 45, 390 I.U.s; sweet potato - 1 medium - 11,940; cooked carrots - 1/2 cup - 8,140; cooked spinach - 1/2 cup - 8,140; cantaloupe - 1/4 medium - 7,290; kale or broccoli (cooked) - 1/2 cup - 4,600; winter squash - 1/2 cup, mashed - 4,300; apricots, fresh - 3 medium - 2,890; watermelon - 1 10-inch slice, 1 inch thick - 2,520. Green leaf lettuce, asparagus, peas, green beans, corn, parsley, and eggs also contain fairly substantial amounts.

You have probably heard that taking too much vitamin A can be dangerous to your health. Perhaps you have heard this about other vitamins, minerals, and amino acids, also. The fact is that you certainly can do yourself a great deal of harm by taking too many supplements, but you would really have to work at it to over-dose on a vitamin from food sources. Eight pounds of carrots eaten by one person in one day for several days would certainly do it! The vitamin A and beta-carotene found in foods converts to a very beneficial vitamin A in the body, but this vitamin A doesn't lead to the side effects that taking too much vitamin A as a supplement can produce. This is true of nearly every vitamin. It is certainly true of vitamin E, which is another vitamin that medical people are always warning us about. Vitamin E found in the body as a result of eating nuts and seeds has never been associated with the bleeding problems during surgery or dental procedures which are occasionally suspected with the high consumption of vitamin E supplements. I have supplemented pregnant women with good, natural vitamin E for many years and have never seen it associated with additional bleeding either during or after the birth. Man-made, laboratory produced, supposedly bio-identical vitamins are of no value at all, and in fact, cause their own set of problems as they clog the receptor sites needed to absorb the real thing.

B-Complex

A couple of things should be mentioned about the B vitamins. The first thing is that they are water-soluble. This means that very little of what you need is stored in the body from day to day. You must ingest—and absorb—what you need on a regular basis. The second thing is that B vitamins are very easily destroyed by heat and/or processing. The milling of a grain can seriously deplete the B vitamin content. The third and most important thing is that B vitamins are team-work vitamins. *They really only work well when sufficient amounts of all of them are available in the body.* This could lead you to believe that supplementation is the only way to go, but finding a well-balanced B-complex supplement is difficult at best, and far too many people find that B vitamin supplements make them nauseous or flatulent.

©**Copyright Butterfly Expressions, llc 2010   Butterfly Miracles with Herbal Remedies**

Roger Williams, Ph.C., D.Sc., a University of Texas chemist and pioneer vitamin researcher, places special emphasis on the team-work principle. "Each B vitamin fits into different parts of the metabolic machinery of every living cell. And like cogs on a wheel, each has a specialized function," he claims.

Sufficient B-complex intake improves nearly every bodily function and organ, and a deficiency can also cause a myriad of problems.

Dr. Williams also explains that to prevent or cure disease, nutrients must also work cooperatively together. "When human beings are fortunate enough to maintain health by consuming wholesome food, this (cooperation) is accomplished by reason of the fact that they consume regularly every one of about 40 nutritional essentials. We utilize in our bodies all nutritional elements simultaneously every day."

The various B vitamins are found in a widely varying list of foods, with the only common denominator from one B vitamin to the next appearing to be brewer's yeast and, possibly, wheat germ. However, since B vitamins are so easily destroyed by processing, a supplement is only as good as its handling. You need to eat a wide variety of foods in as near a whole and natural form as possible if you are to avoid one B vitamin deficiency or another. I believe it can be done, however, especially if you utilize herbs on a daily basis and enjoy herbal teas.

Vitamin C

There is so much that can, and should, be said about vitamin C that many pages would hardly do this amazing and essential nutrient justice. So I have decided to limit this section to part of the research from only two studies. The first study I will quote was conducted by Emil Ginter, Ph.D., a distinguished vitamin C researcher from Czechoslovakia. One aspect of his work concerned the health benefits of having adequate levels of vitamin C in the bloodstream *all* the time.

Maintaining high levels of vitamin C in the blood prevents high cholesterol and builds optimum triglyceride levels. Vitamin C also aids in the absorption of calcium and iron, prevents gallstones, aids the body in detoxifying potentially dangerous histamines, neutralizes unwholesome chemicals in your diet, and is a key factor in wound healing, and much, much more. But humans and animals do not make (synthesize) vitamin C in their own bodies. To reap the benefits of vitamin C in the blood stream requires the continual intake of vitamin C rich foods. Herbs contain significant amount of vitamin C in a very absorbable form.

W. M. Ringsdorf, Jr., D.M.D, of the University of Alabama claims that the RDA of "sixty milligrams is enough, all right—if you want to merely stay just above scurvy level. But if you want to live a life of reduced infection, if you want to promote healing and sharpen your immune system, if you want optimum triglyceride levels in your blood, you'll want a daily intake of Vitamin C far above the RDA." Dr. Ginter believes that in order to keep our reserves of vitamin C at optimum levels, we need about 200 milligrams a day.

Please note here that we are referring to ascorbate acid and not the ascorbic acid that is so often passed off as a vitamin C supplement in today's market.

It should also be noted that stress and environmental pollutants increase the need for vitamin C. There is a long list of drugs, including artificial hormones such as The Pill, etc., phenobarbital, tranquilizers and sleep aids, the glucocorticoid family of anti-inflammatory drugs used to reduce pain in arthritis, and aspirin which interfere with the absorption of vitamin C.

©Copyright Butterfly Expressions, llc 2010   Butterfly Miracles with Herbal Remedies

Foods containing vitamin C include, of course, the citruses, green peppers, papaya, brussels sprouts, broccoli, cantaloupe, cauliflower, strawberries, tomatoes, potatoes, cabbage, and spinach. Eat your fruits and vegetables! Many citruses have been hybridized to maximise the vitamin C content; the vitamin C, however, more closely resembles the very acidic ascorbic acid rather than the more healthy ascorbate acid form. These fruits can be difficult for the body, especially the kidneys, to handle. Herbs are a better source of vitamin C.

Vitamin D

As most people realize, vitamin D is necessary for the uptake of calcium and other minerals. What is not as well known is that you must have vitamin C to uptake the vitamin D you ingest.   Vitamin C is also necessary for the absorption of iron from food sources or supplementation.

Unfortunately, vitamin C is a rather fragile thing. It is easily lost in processing and it fares no better in the body. You must ingest your vitamin C in the same meal as the source of iron or Vitamin D that you are ingesting. In other words, eat your fruits. Just a small amount at a time will be enough if they are fresh. Be sure to eat them often and regularly.

There are many vitamins and minerals that require other vitamins and minerals in order to be absorbed. The wider variety of foods and herbs that you take advantage of, the more likely you will be to get the things that you need from the food that you eat.

Food sources of vitamin D include halibut, cod, mackerel, salmon and tuna.

Vitamin E

Vitamin E is one of the most important of the anti-oxidant nutrient. This vitamin is absolutely essential to the ability of the blood to carry oxygen which in turn affects nearly every organ and system.

At the request of the New York Academy of Sciences, vitamin E experts from all over the world gathered together for three days to educate one another on their individual research projects. Some of their results are listed below.

Improves circulation, especially to the extremities
Eliminates pain in the calves when walking
Improves physical stamina and endurance
Stops the growth/possibly reverses cataracts
Balances the clotting factor in the blood
Protects the lungs from atmospheric pollutants
Raises low HDL levels
May increase resistance to disease
Protects against heart disease
Increases oxygen in the bloodstream (and to the
    placenta during pregnancy)

Protects against environmental pollutants
Relieves nighttime leg and foot muscle cramps
Protects cell membranes from destruction
Heals abrasions, cuts and scars
Cold sores
Helps the body manage stress
May help prevent breast cancer

Sources of vitamin E included wheat germ oil, sunflower seeds, most nuts, lobster, salmon, and peanut butter.

©Copyright Butterfly Expressions, llc 2010   Butterfly Miracles with Herbal Remedies

What Vitamins Need in Order to be Absorbed
(A Few Simple Concepts for 'Fuel Efficiency')

The following basic rules apply both to the nutrients in your food and any supplements you might choose to take.

▶   Some vitamins need fat to be absorbed. Vitamins A, D, E, and K are on this list. Without fat, vitamin E is not absorbed by the body at all. Fat-containing foods also prolong absorption, preventing spikes that are followed by insufficient vitamin C available to the cells. Even the water soluble vitamins like B-complex and C need some fat to be absorbed. In other words, without some *good* fats in your diet you will not absorb sufficient nutrients from the foods you eat or the supplements you take. What is not absorbed will be excreted without doing your body any good at all. Slower absorption will result in increased levels of the nutrients in your blood over a longer period of time.

Every nutritional requirement that the human body has operates on a twenty-four hour cycle. Your cells do not go to sleep when you do, nor can they survive without a continuous supply of oxygen and nutrients.

Some nutrients just naturally go together:

▶   Iron from plant sources needs vitamin C to be absorbed and it has to be taken at the same time (during the same meal)! Fortunately, many plants that contain iron also contain vitamin C.

▶   Folic Acid containing compounds must be split by an enzyme before the folate can be absorbed. This enzyme requires sufficient zinc, preferably from foods or meals that contain both zinc and folic acid.

▶   Iron absorption can be seriously reduced by the presence of the common preservative EDTA. I wonder what havoc other preservatives are creating!?!

▶   The continued use of stimulants such as caffeine seriously and negatively affects the absorption capabilities of the digestive tract.

▶   A relaxed atmosphere during mealtime and a quiet period immediately afterwards aids digestion. It does little good to put in good food and then prevent its digestion because of stress.

▶   Exercise will give your digestive system the same benefits that it gives the rest of your body. If exercise is not a part of your day, your cells are probably not getting sufficient oxygen to perform their functions. Mild exercise that is aimed at using stomach and abdominal muscles is particularly effective.

▶   **A high quality diet will substantially help you get the good things that you need!**

▶   Supplements, as a general rule, are best taken with other foods and minerals. This cannot be overemphasized. Taken on an empty stomach, most supplements pass right through your body with very little being absorbed. Primed by something as simple as a piece of fruit or a slice of whole wheat bread, digestive enzymes are ready to go to work on the supplements.

©**Copyright Butterfly Expressions, llc 2010   Butterfly Miracles with Herbal Remedies**

Will you get enough nutrition from food alone?

Most of the horror stories that you have heard about how cooking and processing breaks down nutrients are probably true. For example, vitamin C is very sensitive to oxygen; once you remove the peel, vitamin C immediately begins to escape. Milling whole grain products to produce white flour removes 70 to 80 percent of the valuable vitamins and minerals. The argument can certainly be made that the vitamins being put back in are not biologically active, and therefore, of no use to the body at all. Baking soda and **chlorine** added to the water in which vegetables are cooked destroys most of the thiamine (thiamine was the only nutrient tested for in this study). What this means, basically, is that government—or anybody else's—nutritional tables may or may not reflect what you are getting of a particular nutrient. Just because a nutrient was originally there and is listed on the label, doesn't necessarily mean that you are getting it.

Personally, I believe that God is good and there is more than enough to spare in his creations. But very little of this earth is as God made it and nutrition is very important. Our modern diet, with its refining and processing, often contains more sodium than we need and less potassium, zinc, selenium, chromium, silicon, and nickel. We add too many extra calories in the form of sugar and indigestible fats in relation to minerals and vitamins. It might be a fun exercise to muscle test yourself from time to time—for an average day—and see if you are getting enough of various vitamins and minerals. I find this very educational, and too often, quite alarming!

Vitamin Bandits or Vitamin Antagonists, as they are officially known.

There are so many of these that it is probably foolish to believe that our bodies are getting all of the nutrients promised by those tidy little charts.

▶ Life's ordinary circumstances, such as stress, advanced age, disease, illness (even a slight head cold), pregnancy, lack of sleep, increased physical activity, can all use up a significant amount of the body's vitamin reserves and require constant replenishing.

▶ Refined carbohydrates such as white sugar and flour have most of the B vitamins refined right out of them during the milling process. But because thiamine and others in the B complex are needed to make an enzyme used in the burning of carbohydrates, these vitamins have to be taken from the liver or other storage places in order for the carbohydrates you have just eaten to be properly metabolized. Refined carbohydrates not only contain no nutrients, but they actually rob the body of nutrients that would be better utilized doing something besides metabolizing sweets. *Natural carbohydrates come equipped with their own B vitamin supply, so they don't pilfer the body's store when being processed.*

▶ Black tea, the kind the Word of Wisdom warns against, contains tannins that destroy or inactivate B vitamins. The same thing is true of most teas promoted as *green* tea. *Remember, B vitamins are linked to nerve health and the ability to withstand stress.*

▶ There are over 3,000 chemicals used in the production of our Nation's food supply. These chemicals affect your nutrition in several ways. They enhance the development of enzymes that destroy certain vitamins. Chemicals cause excessive elimination of certain nutrients by the body. They also impair your body's ability to absorb certain nutrients because, chemically, they are just similar enough to block the cell's receptor sites for that nutrient.

▶ Insecticide residues and pollutants in the air can interfere with our body's vitamin reserves and absorption.

▶ Even vitamins can sometimes act as antagonists. Large amounts of a single member of the B complex may increase your need for others in the B-complex group because the excess of the one causes the body to excrete them all; they travel linked together in nature. You end up with too little of the ones you didn't take extra of.

©Copyright Butterfly Expressions, llc 2010   Butterfly Miracles with Herbal Remedies

Some of the Ways Drugs Disrupt Your Nutritional Balance

▶   Boric acid latches onto one of the proteins of riboflavin (a B vitamin) and then excretes it from the body through the urine. The missing riboflavin protein upsets the balance of the B vitamins. The body, using the lower amount as a gauge, brings the B vitamins back into balance by excreting the ones it now considers to be in excess, even though there may actually not be enough of them for the body's needs. *Boric acid is present in at least 400 home products, including mouth washes and toothpastes.*

▶   Other drugs and artificial hormones follow the same procedure as that outlined above for boric acid. Tranquilizers and sleeping aids lower the amount of calcium in the blood by disrupting the metabolism of vitamin D. Phenobarbital has been linked to cases of softening of the bone caused by lack of calcium. These little nasties also increase the excretion of vitamin C from the body.

▶   Glucocorticoids is the family of anti-inflammatory drugs most often prescribed to relieve the symptoms of arthritis. A listed side effect of this family of drugs is osteoporosis, a classic calcium deficiency disease. ***These drugs are also used on children in the treatment of kidney disease and have been linked to potassium deficiency and low levels of vitamin C.***

▶   Digitalis increases the body's need for thiamine, and thus, all of the B vitamins.

▶   Hydralazine, used for high blood pressure, can create a B vitamin deficiency.

▶   Diuretics, used to counter high blood pressure, can flush enough potassium out of the system to create a serious imbalance. The diuretic Triamterene works without depleting potassium, but it interferes with the utilization of folic acid. Diuretics produce excessive excretions of calcium and other minerals.

▶   Mineral oils, used in over-the-counter laxatives, block normal absorption in the digestive tract. Mineral oil dissolves carotene without allowing the body to utilize this A vitamin. It also interferes with all of the fat-soluble vitamins—A, D, E, and K.

▶   Even a small dose of aspirin can cause the excretion of vitamin C to triple. Aspirin also disrupts the utilization of folic acid.

▶   Antihistamines destroy nearly 40% of the existing vitamin A in the bloodstream.

▶   'The Pill' is an artificial hormone. It allows an egg to be fertilized, but creates hormonal imbalances that prevent implantation. This hormone imbalance creates a situation in which vitamin C and some of the B-complex vitamins are depleted as they are utilized in the body's effort to re-establish hormone balance. Because of the shortage of B vitamins, depression is a frequent result. Lowered resistance to infection and less ability to handle stress are also frequent side effects of this form of birth control.

Enough of this soap box!! These are only a few examples; I could go on all day on this topic.

Subclinical Malnutrition

Studies done at the School of Gerontology, University of Southern California, indicate that if a person has a sub-clinical nutritional deficiency, he or she might appear perfectly normal ***except for*** an increased susceptibility to disease, longer recovery time from surgery, adverse reactions to flu vaccines, extreme fatigue that interferes with normal functioning, depression, insomnia, and irritability. ***Perfectly normal?***

Richard Revlin, M.D., of the Sloan-Kettering Cancer institute says, *"In the United States today, we rarely see cases of classical vitamin deficiency, such as scurvy and pellagra. But we are now beginning to recognize a vast new series of marginal deficiencies related to disease . . . Marginal deficiency, it now appears, may be a surprisingly common phenomenon."*

©**Copyright Butterfly Expressions, llc 2010   Butterfly Miracles with Herbal Remedies**

Effects of Subclinical Malnutrition

To understand what happens in our bodies when we are deficient in a certain vitamin or mineral, we would need to first understand what role that vitamin or mineral plays in our health.   The education required of doctors, hospital dieticians, nurses, etc., appears to be woefully inadequate where nutrition is concerned, in my opinion. And certainly, the young women of today—who will be the mothers of tomorrow—have very little in their high school or college curriculum that will prepare them to adequately nourish their future families.

This is a complicated topic, and though I have read voraciously on the subject, I am certainly not an expert. I have learned enough to know, however, that nutrition is vitally important to our health, both physically and mentally.

Vitamin A

skin problems
lack of immune function with
   increased susceptibility to colds
dryness in the mucous
   membranes of respiratory and
   urinary area
less stress resistance
tire more easily

experiences low healing of
wounds
less efficient detoxing from
      poisonous chemicals
excessive menstruation
infertility in men
middle ear infections
cyst-like masses in middle ear

night blindness or blurring
glaucoma
crohn's disease
tooth decay in infants & children
increased risk of heart disease
high blood pressure
increased risk of stroke
peptic ulcer

B Vitamins - the teamwork vitamins
   (Never supplement just one B vitamin at a time - always use in a balanced complex)

Thiamine (just one B vitamin)
vague, general symptoms
lack of appetite
craving for sweets and junk food
indigestion
nausea
severe constipation

heart muscle weakness
edema
neuropathy and paralysis
brain and nervous disorders
difficulties with memory
seizures

neurosis
a high percentage of cancer
   patients test low for thiamine
glaucoma and vision
   disturbances

Vitamin E

lack of circulation, especially to the hands and
   feet
pain and cramping in the muscles
lack of physical stamina and endurance
problems with the clotting of the blood
lowered resistance to disease
wrinkles and other signs of the destruction of
   cellular membranes
slow healing of cuts and scrapes
inability to handle stress

shortened life span
hormonal problems, especially at menopause
poor circulation along the neural pathways
anemia
poor absorption and utilization of fats
chronic diarrhea and bloating
degeneration of nerves
muscle weakness
visual field constriction
if severe, can contribute to heart arrhythmias

©Copyright Butterfly Expressions, llc 2010   Butterfly Miracles with Herbal Remedies

Body Systems Analysis Charts

System/Function	Diseases	Symptoms	Stressors	Vit/Mins/Foods	Herbs/Supplements
Circulatory heart (cardio-pulmonary) arteries veins *Carries nourishment to every cell of the body*	anemia bruising palpitations hemorrhoids nosebleeds Raynaud's stroke varicose veins	chest pain fatigue on climbing anxiety swelling in lower legs and feet restlessness dizziness	unchecked virus stress caffeine all drugs sugar uric acid congested liver, colon or kidneys intestinal toxemia food allergies xanthine oxidase (present in homogenized milk, damaging to heart muscle)	potassium calcium (regulating of heartbeat and blood clotting) magnesium (particularly for irregular heartbeat) onions oats potatoes carrots barley olive oil	L-Carnitine L-Arginine digestive enzymes butchers broom gingko biloba hawthorn pleurisy root rosehips gentian cayenne garlic ginger dandelion root
Lymphatic tonsils appendix lymph nodes spleen *Carries nutrients & detoxifies the body. Lymph fluid goes deep into the body tissues where blood cannot penetrate. If the lymph gets overburdened, waste gets stored in the connective tissue of organs and joints*	cancer tonsillitis allergies sinusitis arthritis colitis lupus skin disorders	fluid retention loss of energy constipation low back pain sluggish thinking Babies: acquired through infection & drugs prenatally - constant colds runny nose, earaches *all itching is lymph related*	removal of the tonsils environmental poisons drug residues subclinical malnutrition	*Exercise is vital* vitamin A vitamin C vitamin D B-Complex vitamins lemons cabbage cloves parsley carrots honey mustard onions watercress	enzymes thyme ginger myrrh sage echinacea garlic rosemary calendula rehamania root elecampane

System/Function	Diseases	Symptoms	Stressors	Vit/Mins/Foods	Herbs/Supplements

Digestive
stomach
gall bladder
small intestine
colon
liver
 	
absorbing nutrients
 	
It is estimated that 80%
of ailments begin in
a toxic & constipated
colon. Poisons from
the colon can stress the
heart, lodge in joints,
invade muscles, cause
fatigue & weakness,
create skin problems,
irritate the lungs and
drastically overtax the
liver.
	anorexia
	bad breath
	dyspepsia
	gallstones
	gingivitis
	heartburn
	hiatal hernia
	motion sickness
	tooth decay
	ulcers
	candida
	colitis
	constipation
	diarrhea
	diverticulitis
		Intestinal:
		aching muscles
		headaches
		indigestion
		belching
		excessive gas
		heartburn
		abdominal pain
		bloating
		nausea
		acid stomach
		
		Liver:
		fatigue
		loss of appetite
		waking (1-3 am)
		light colored stools
			emotional stress
			antacids
			antibiotics
			tranquilizers
			sleep aids
			blood pressure
			  medications
			pepto-bismal
			pepcid & tagamet
			aspirin
			atropine
			  (motion sickness
			  medication)
			anti-depressants
			
			Laxatives can cause
			lazy bowel. They
			are habit forming
			& cause depletion
			of minerals such as
			potassium which can
			then lead to heart
			attacks.
				whole grains
				vegetables
				fruits
				nuts and seeds
				
				Liver:
				potassium
					Intestinal/
					stomach:acidophilus
					enzymes
					
					cascara sagrada
					slippery elm bark
					plantain
					papaya
					elecampane
					peppermint
					fennel
					catnip
					cramp bark
					
					Liver:
					rosemary
					calendula
					dandelion root
					yellow dock root
					burdock
					raw beet root

Liver: All drugs and pollutants damage and overstress the liver because of its function as the collection place for toxins, etc.

Cancer cannot develop in the body if the liver is functioning in an efficient and healthy manner.

System/Function	Diseases	Symptoms	Stressors	Vits/Mins/Foods	Herbs/ Supplements
Integumentary skin hair nails sweat glands *Health of the hair, nails & skin is an indication of the over-all health of the entire body.* Low thyroid function is often the cause of hair loss. ***A great deal of what we put on the skin is absorbed into the body!!***	hair loss acne abscess athlete's foot baldness burns corns/callouses cysts dandruff nail problems psoriasis warts wrinkles skin cancer fungal infections	varied according to what part of the system is affected White spots on nails indicate a lack of minerals or poor assimilation of nutrients. Ridges going lengthwise in the nails can indicate anemia (or anemia in the past) or a lack of B-vitamins, calcium, silica, sulfur and/or protein. Brittle nails can be an indication of the lack of B-vitamins, iron, or silica *(consider the homeopathic remedy Silicea for these symptoms.*	chemicals harsh detergents rich greasy fried foods sugar stress lack of sleep	Vitamin A is an effective treatment for most skin disorders. B-complex vitamin C vitamin E The better the diet, the better will be the skin, hair & nails	Skin: all diaphoretic herbs (sweat producing) Hair: rosemary calendula nettles horsetail parsley Blond hair rinse: chamomile yarrow calendula mullein flowers Brown hair rinse: elderberries Dandruff: rinse with one or more of the above herbs (using the essential oil form is nice - but it only takes a drop or two)

System/Function	Diseases	Symptoms	Stressors	Vits/Mins/Foods	Herbs/Supplements

Nervous
brain
nerves
 	
The central nervous system is the spinal cord and brain.
The peripheral nervous system is the nerves that extend out from the spinal cord and the base of the brain to other parts of the body. The autonomic nervous system regulates the internal organs.
 	
The central nervous system and the immune system are closely related. The brain sends messages back & forth between the two systems.
	alzheimer's
	anorexia
	autism
	bulimia
	depression
	down's syndrome
	dyslexia
	epilepsy
	meningitis
	multiple
	  sclerosis
	parkinson's
	senility
	shingles
	spina bifida
		Varied according to the area of the body affected.
		
		Symptoms can include mental illness and dementia.
		
		headaches
		hyperactivity
		insomnia
		memory loss
		vertigo
			most sensitive organs
			
			react poorly to poor nutrition, lack of oxygen, prescription drugs, air pollution, poor food and water, stress, toxic metals
			
			problem drugs:
			ativan (anxiety & tension drug)
			bitolterol (asthma)
			bromocriptine (prevention of lactation after birth)
			cyclobenzaprine (muscle relaxant)
				B-complex
				vitamin C
				calcium
				
				whole grains
				green leafy
				  vegetables
				nuts
				seeds
				molasses
					blue vervain
					cayenne
					damiana
					gotu kola
					dong quai
					lady slipper
					motherwort
					passion flower
					hops
					black cohosh
					skullcap
					catnip
					chamomile
					peppermint
					hawthorn berries
					
					oats
					lavender
					pulsatilla
					St. Johns wort
					lemon balm
					ginseng
					lobelia
					valerian
					wood betony

System/Function	Diseases	Symptoms	Stressors	Vits/Mins/Foods	Herbs/Summplements
Respiratory nose throat trachea bronchials lungs *The lungs are one of the main channels of elimination in the body. They also provide oxygen to the blood so that it can be carried to all the cells. Metabolism in all body organs is stimulated with the intake of oxygen. Trouble in the respiratory tract can impair immune function.*	allergies asthma bronchitis coughs chest pain colds, croup emphysema flu hay fever laryngitis pleurisy pneumonia sinusitis tuberculosis	varied and many	pollutants such as lead, ozone, carbon monoxide congestion in the bowels and liver repressed emotions being 'smothered' by another person **problem drugs:** Pindolol (high blood pressure) Hydralazine (hypertension) Ketroprofen (anti-inflammatory) too much red meat	vitamin A vitamin E B-complex all minerals salmon oil flaxseed oil lecithin	eucalyptus - especially the essential oil comfrey mullein marshmallow ephedra horehound wild cherry rosehips aloe vera
Structural bones muscles cartilage *When we have aches and pains of the bones, muscles and ligaments, the body is trying to warn us that something is wrong and needs our immediate attention. When we have dealt with the underlying causes, the pain will go away.*	arthritis carpal tunnel bursitis fractures gout lumbago muscle cramps muscular dystrophy osteoporosis rheumatism scoliosis sprains swelling TMJ	**Pain** bruising inflammation injured ligaments	lack of nutrients in the diet caffeine, soda pop too much protein/meat sugar (leaches calcium & essential minerals) emotional stress **problem drugs:** Cortisone like steroids (which strip potassium) can cause diseases where bone fragility is manifested and contribute to heart disease.	B-complex silica calcium magnesium vitamin D minerals vitamin A (teeth) **sunlight** (needed for bone health - not a lot, but consistently)	oats horsetail nettles comfrey mullein white oak bark

System/Function	Diseases	Symptoms	Stressors	Vits/Mins/Foods	Herbs/Supplements
Urinary kidneys bladder *The kidneys are the chief organs for cleansing the body's internal fluid. They keep the system in balance by controlling composition and volume of the blood. They maintain the electrolyte balance & manufacture hormones that regulate blood pressure, calcium metabolism and red blood cell production*	bed wetting urinary tract infections cystitis kidney stones high blood pressure stroke heart attack glaucoma	Symptoms of early kidney problems are: pain pallor swelling in extremities headaches high blood pressure blood in urine burning & stinging	alcohol drugs (even prescription) infections surgery obesity	alcohol drugs (even prescription) infections surgery obesity	corn silk cleavers plantain chamomile horsetail juniper parsley hydrangea goldenrod uva ursi buchu marshmallow
Immune **drugs that weaken:** vaccinations (all come with a built-in immune suppressant) antibiotics tranquilizers sleeping pills hypertension medication *The immune system is the body's defense against viral and bacterial diseases. It also protects us from damage created by an out-of-balance system—to some extent.*	AIDS allergies cancer candida epstein-barre gastritis lupus (more than 50 medication list lupus as a side effect!) Toxic shock many others		See first column for drugs pesticides heavy metals toxins chlorine stress refined oils caffeine Dionxin (a widely used chlorine bleach, used in industries to whiten products such as toilet paper, paper towels, milk cartons, tea bags, paper plates & cups)	L-arginine L-Lysine vitamin C B-complex bioflavonoids magnesium calcium	echinacea garlic goldenseal oregon grape lemon balm St. Johns wort thyme hyssop rosemary nettles plantain bayberry calendula myrrh poke root

The Endocrine (or Glandular) System

When the glands do not receive the needed nutrients, they over-stimulate the digestive organs and demand more food because they are not nutritionally satisfied. This causes an unhealthy appetite, food cravings, and over-secretion of hormones which finally results in exhaustion of the hormone producing glands.

The following drugs contribute to glandular problems on every level. I did not want to list them under each organ (over and over again) so I am putting them here:

Corticosteriods are used for skin conditions such as eczema and hives. Generically, they are known as **Tricycllic antidepressants.** Prozac is a leader among this nasty group of drugs.

Indomethacin is an ingredient in anti-inflammatories and topical analgesics (pain relief gels & creams).

Gland/Function	Diseases	Symptoms	Stressors	Vits/Mins/Foods	Herbs/ Supplements
Adrenals *protect us from stress improves digestion*	addison's cushing's cystic fibrosis hyperthyroid hypoglycemia mononucleosis pancreatitis parathyroid	aching joints weakness lethargy dizziness headaches memory problems food craving allergies blood sugar disorders	cortisone therapy continual & prolonged stress poor nutritional habits smoking alcohol and drug abuse	balanced diet B vitamins calcium magnesium potassium zinc	kelp devil's claw bilberry hawthorne safflowers licorice astragalus ginseng papaya avoid: goldenseal
Thymus *Produces T-cells which destroy foreign microbes. Helps create a positive outlook.*	depression fatigue	crankiness lack of energy	vaccinations, pollution & drugs are particularly hard on the thymus large in children; small in adults Why????	balanced diet zinc sleep rest	kelp

Gland/Function	Diseases/Symptoms	Stressors	Vits/Mins/Foods	Herbs/Supplements
Pineal *Nerve impulses from the pineal gland are fed to the hypothalamus and pituitary glands. The pineal gland affects blood pressure, body temperature, motor function, reproduction, sleep patterns, collagen, enzymes, and body cycles. The pineal directly affects every other gland of the body and the cardiovascular system.*	depression discontent feelings of self-doubt sleep disorders mood swings	Sunlight (or full-spectrum artificial light) triggers retinal nerve impulses which then travel to the pineal gland and on to the other glands in the body.	minerals whole foods diet B-complex calcium magnesium	kelp nettle alfalfa ginseng
Pituitary *The pituitary gland is the master gland which gives instructions to all the other glands telling them how much to produce and how to function,.The pituitary gland protects us from fatigue due to mental stress*	mental fatigue trembling	much the same as the adrenals and thymus	vitamin E B-complex manganese selenium trace minerals amino acids	kelp ginseng nettles goto kola alfalfa
Pancreas *The pancreas is vital to digestion, maintenance of blood sugar levels & activating enzyme activity*	all blood sugar related symptoms: headache blurred vision etc.	drugs mental & emotional stress	B-complex minerals chromium selenium manganese sodium amino acids	cedar berries licorice root uva ursi mullein bilberries blueberries alfalfa juniper berries saw palmetto oregon grape

Gland/Function	Diseases/Symptoms	Stressors	Vits/Mins/Foods	Herbs/Supplements
Thyroid *The thyroid regulates metabolism in the body and is considered another master gland because it sends instructions to other glands and organs.*	either excessive heat (hyper) or excessive cold (hypo) physical & mental fatigue nervousness obesity sluggishness puffy face hair loss high cholesterol levels	over-work type A personality drugs lack of nutrition	B-complex minerals iodine potassium sodium amino tyrosine	kelp/dulce Irish moss black walnut white oak bark gentian nettles alfalfa
Hypothalamus communication between nerves and glands *The hypothalamus regulates the network of glands and the nervous system.*	trouble in the hypothalamus causes imbalances in the entire glandular and hormonal systems with every nasty symptom of that imbalance	all of the things that have been listed as having a negative impact on the other glands	over all good nutrition and vitamin supplementation	ginseng sarsaparilla gotu kola fo-ti saw palmetto nettles

Adrenals: The adrenal glands control water and mineral balance in the cells of the body, are responsible for resistance to stress, and are vital to immune function, and the regulation of blood pressure.

Pituitary: The pituitary produces the hormones that are essential to fertility. The pituitary induces ovulation and maintains pregnancy, controls lactation, and produces estrogen for prevention of symptoms associated with menopause. Communications from this gland stimulate the thyroid and adrenals and is an essential part of normal growth. The pituitary maintains hair growth and good health

Thyroid: The thyroid regulates oxygen in the blood, regulates the burning of calories, and controls growth and development of bones, nerves, and muscles. The thyroid also controls the rate of absorption of calcium and other minerals

Thyroid tests can indicate, falsely, that the thyroid function is normal because of the presence of shampoos & skin antiseptic compounds

Symptoms of thyroid deficiency are slow reaction time, acne, frequent colds, fatigue w/headaches, chronic boils, menstrual disorders w/o cysts, fear, panic, forgetfulness, depression that is worse in winter (thyroid must work harder in winter to step up metabolism to combat cold temperatures), poor equilibrium, muscle aches, weakness, some hearing and nervous system disorders leading to burning or prickly sensations, lack of concentration, and anemia. *Low thyroid* function is directly related to heart attacks and lung disease. Treatment for the thyroid can prevent these illnesses.

Hypothalamus: The hypothalamus governs the liver, heart, pituitary and the reception of messages from the brain. The messages are then passed along to organs such as the thyroid. The hypothalamus is responsible for aging, regulates autonomic responses (no conscious effort—functions such as heartbeat and breathing, etc.). Thy hypothalamus also produces hormones and enzymes. It is responsible for fluid regulation, sleep patterns, heart contractions, and temperature. ***The hypothalamus coordinates the entire endocrine system.***

Parathyroid: The parathyroid regulates calcium levels by promoting the release of calcium from bones. Malfunction of the parathyroid produces osteoporosis. The parathyroid regulates the levels of all nutrients in the body; malfunction of the parathyroid decreases mineral absorption dramatically.

Additional Information

Urinary: All 'itis' (including arthritis) is related to the kidneys. To correct situations of this type, it is essential to cleanse the kidneys and the liver and to support the adrenal glands and the spleen. All heart pathology also has its inception in the kidneys. The kidneys and adrenals, and indirectly, the thyroid regulate blood pressure by sending signals to the adrenals to produce the necessary precursors. *The primary function of the Urinary System is to keep the entire system in balance by controlling the composition and volume of the blood.*

Digestive:
Liver: The liver performs over 500 functions. A clogged liver is the cause of enzyme deficiencies; it is wise to cleanse and support this organ. The liver secretes bile and stores nutrients until there is a need for them. The liver draws off and stores toxins until they can be eliminated from the body. Bile from the liver breaks down fats and is necessary for the absorption of vitamins and calcium. Proper liver function promotes peristalsis. If you are constipated, consider a mild liver cleanse. Constipation, in turn, causes serious stress on the liver. This can become a vicious cycle. Liver malfunction is a known cause of hypothyroidis. The liver is important in the regulation of blood sugar. It breaks down hormones like adrenalin, etc., when the need for them by the body is over. In other words, the liver helps the body return to normal following a period of high stress. High potassium foods aid the liver. Kelp, dulce, molasses, rice, wheat bran, raisins, and bananas all contain large quantities of potassium. Other causes of problems in the liver: 1) cumulative environmental poisons, 2) high carbohydrate/fat diet, 3) overeating, 4) drugs, 5) candida, 6) contraception, 7) caffeine

Small intestine: The small intestine is the site of absorption for most nutrients.

Colon: Some nutrients are absorbed by the blood vessels through the walls of the colon and then carried by the bloodstream to the liver. From the liver they are dispersed throughout the body. Crud along the colon walls drastically reduces nutritional uptake.

There are places in the colon (rectal area, mostly) where absorption bypasses the liver. This means that bacteria and toxins from the constipated rectal area of the colon enters the bloodstream and is able to reach all the organs of the body. These circulating nasties in the blood are called endotoxins. This dirty blood may even contain cancer cells! Evacuating the colon when the need first occurs prevents the occurrence of much of this kind of absorption.

There is a reservoir in the colon designed to handle one meal at a time. As the next meal approaches, the current meal presses against a neural plexus call the Olsen Point, which activates a complex of peristaltic muscles. Between meal snacks really fouls up this process and contributes to constipation.

Colon Health: To achieve and maintain colon health it is advisable to choose foods wisely, take time to chew, avoid between meal snacks, and take time to visit the bathroom three times daily—after each meal.

Appendix: The appendix releases enzymes which contribute to a good fermentation process in the colon.

Very Basic Chinese Body Systems Analysis

The Chinese do not really think of the body as a series of organs. When they think liver, for example, they are thinking of the meridians that support this organ, the related lymph system, muscle, nerve, and vascular systems, etc., and all of the emotions and environmental factors that affect the liver and are reflected by it.

Kidney   The kidney affects reproduction, growth and the regeneration of cells. The kidney meridian and organ have much to do with the health of our teeth, bones, bone marrow, brain, inner ear, pupil of eye, and the lumbar regions of the back. Emotionally, kidney energy is associated with fear, the will—meaning both will power and the ability to make and follow through on decisions. The kidneys and the affiliated system affect our perception and our ability to think clearly and sharply.

Heart   The heart in eastern philosophy houses spirit. From the heart the soul of man governs the mind. It does this by drawing conclusions about lessons learned from past traumas and postulating what is possible for the future.

Spleen   The spleen is responsible for the assimilation of foods, fluids, and ***ideas.***

                Problems in the spleen create tension in the neck and shoulders, high blood pressure, headaches, cramping, moodiness, and impulsive behavior.

Lung   The lungs set the basic rhythms of the body and draw in inspiration. Breathing deeply and calmly is one of the best things you can do for your general health.

                Congestion in the lungs or failure to breathe deeply can create tightness in the chest, contribute to skin rashes, and increase the frequency and duration of colds and flu. Rigid thinking and melancholy can be a contributory factor to problems in this area. This type of thinking and feeling can also be a result of chronic congestion in the lungs.

All illness results from a depletion or congestion of Chi.

Depletion   Depletion of Chi creates muscle weakness, lethargy, frequent illness, poor digestion, and inadequate blood flow.

Congestion   Congestion of Chi results in muscle and joint pain, tension, tenderness, pain, a distended abdomen, swelling of tissues, and irritability of temperament.

Chapter Three
Herbs as Nutrition

Why a discussion of nutrition and vitamin deficiencies in a booklet about herbal remedies?

Because—and I want you to write this somewhere prominent in your memories—

One basic reason herbal remedies work for a particular problem is that the herb has provided one or more vital nutrients that are missing in the diet.

Ninety percent of the herbs that I use fall, very definitely, into nutritional categories. I seriously wonder if the other ten percent would be categorized as nutritional too if we understood them better! I believe even the nervine herbs and herbs that are considered anti-depressant work predominantly on nutritional principles. Even the heavy-duty infection fighters seem to follow these principles, to a great extent.

Herbs are not witchcraft or magic wands. They are a source of vitamins and trace minerals. Let's look at the very common herb, marshmallow. On an average, a cup of tea made from the fresh herb checks in with 249 mg of calcium, 12.7 mg of iron (that is very high), and 2,190 IU's of vitamin A. A well-dried herbal product would be slightly less nutritious. Used in tea or tincture form, the nutrients are readily absorbed and available almost immediately to the body. Another great herb, nettle, checks in with 6,500 IU's of vitamin A, putting it right up there with the very best foods. Nettle also contains a whooping amount of vitamin C.

As we have demonstrated in the previous chapters, vitamins and minerals (or the lack of them) play a dynamic role in your health. But, because herbals work on nutritional principles, how quickly they work for you depends on a variety of factors:

- how nutritionally deficient you were in the first place
- your body's ability to absorb and utilize the herbal nutrition you are giving it
- how much your life style and heredity demand from you nutritionally
- What vitamin bandits are at work in your life (low grade infections, lots of sugar, too little sleep, drugs, high stress levels - the list goes on and on).
- the potency of the herbs you use (just like foods, herbs can lose their nutritional content by poor processing methods and improper storage
- How well the eliminative organs (including your skin) are doing their job. A toxic colon or kidneys that do not filter properly can put a great amount of toxins back into the blood stream. This interferes with the uptake of vitamins and minerals, while at the same time, increasing the need for them.

I have seen demonstrated, time after time over the years, that herbs seem to work far better on people who have been doing herbs for a while. At first I thought that this was because new people were not proficient in the use of herbs. I would try to work more closely with each family for a while as they began using herbal remedies. Eventually, I realized that there were other factors involved. Some of these factors were: 1) Their bodies needed to eliminate the poisons (drugs, etc.) that were blocking much of the absorption of the herbal vitamins and minerals. This often takes quite a bit of time and effort. 2) The colon and kidneys needed to be in good working order. As the overall nutrition of a body increases, dead and diseased tissue that is being replaced by healthy tissue sluffs off. It needs a clear channel of elimination. Otherwise, it re-enters the bloodstream and auto-intoxication develops. In other words, the little nasties collect along the brain stem, form gallstones, etc., or simply return to the liver. 3) As toxins, drugs, etc., leave the body, they do so by combining with certain nutrients. This means, that in people beginning to use herbs, *the extra nutrition is being used for a cleansing program, rather than a re-building program,* until the house cleaning has been accomplished. Sometimes people will feel the mild effects of this cure and become quite discouraged.

©Copyright Butterfly Expressions, llc 2010   Butterfly Miracles with Herbal Remedies

Some Basic Herbal Knowledge and Lore:

• Herbs feed the body, much like food *should*. They should aid the bodies natural healing processes by providing essential nutrients.

• Herbs work without the toxic side effects associated with drugs because they have been left in their natural state—unaltered by chemical processes. Herbs contain elements in the amounts that nature intended. Built right into the plant are both the elements (vitamins and minerals) needed to make the plant effective and the elements that act as safe-guards. For example, it is almost impossible to take enough lobelia, in any herbal form, for the narcotic principles to slow your heart because, built right into the plant, are elements that would cause you to vomit and throw off the excess. This is true of MaHuang, also, but because it caused problems in a chemically altered state, we can no longer purchase this wonderful herb.

• The so-called active constituents of many herbs have been isolated by modern science. Many of them are the basis of common drugs. Researchers have been dismayed to discover that in many instances the isolated constituent was less active biologically than the original herb. (Why are they dismayed? Perhaps, because there is no economic reward to the pharmaceutical firm who paid for the research!)

• There is no standardization program for herbal extracts, at least not one that is being applied very widely. A company who makes tinctures or herbal capsules, for instance, does not always need to meet standards of potency or list potency on the label. (This is fine with me, because in order to do so they would have to isolate the compounds and then they would act like, and be, drugs!) What this means to you, though, is that everything you buy for the benefits of, say mullein, may not have the important properties of mullein. For this reason, making your own herbal medicines from plant materials that are still potent (they make your nose tickle) is the only way to be sure of potency.

• Generally the action of an herb is gradual and subtle. Healing takes place at its own pace. There are notable exceptions!! The body often responds quite readily to even a little improvement in overall nutrition.

• Herbs, like vegetables, are alkaline. Certain bacteria and disease states cannot thrive in an alkaline environment. The addition of herbs to the diet improves the bodies acid/alkaline balance.

• ***Most herbs in use are extremely safe!*** In the 1970's, when herbs began their rise in popularity, numerous articles appearing in medical journals and magazines questioned the safety of herbal products. Since then, herbal usage has increased dramatically, but toxicity reports have not. Actual research, not medical or pharmaceutical scare tactics, have consistently demonstrated the safety of herbal medicines. Investigative reporters continually conclude that there is a total lack of substantial evidence that toxic reactions to herbal products are a major concern. ***(Would that drugs had the same record!)*** Ephedra has been much in the news lately, but you will notice that the reported deaths have occurred from some pretty refined and laboratory-altered products. These products have been so altered in laboratories that they more closely resemble drugs than an herbal remedy. I have used ephedra safely for many years, but because of reactions to this drug made from the herb, we can no longer purchase this magnificent plant.

• Do not interpret the above statement to mean that all plants are safe to use as medicines. There are extremely poisonous and toxic plants out there. If you are going to harvest your own, know what you are doing. Always buy your dried herbs from reliable sources—they need to know what they are doing, too.

©Copyright Butterfly Expressions, llc 2010   **Butterfly Miracles with Herbal Remedies**

Herbs, in books and study courses, are not indexed according to their nutritional value. Rather they are classified by their predominant effect on the body. Unless you intend to study nutrition, health, and disease in-depth and can find reliable information on the nutritive values of herbs (I've tried - unsuccessfully), classification by effect is probably the only viable method. Since classification by effect is the standard throughout the world, that is the method I will use here.

There is, however, one drawback to this system of classification; an herb may have several different effects and work on several different body systems. It becomes difficult—actually impossible—to pick just one category for some herbs. Another herbal characteristic that makes classification difficult is the fact that herbs, unlike drugs, act as stabilizing agents. In other words, cayenne may be used to stop the flow of blood or to increase circulation, and the same herbal combination will be used to lower high blood pressure and to raise low blood pressure.

In contrast to drugs, herbs are natural and safe. They do not build up in the body producing horrendous side effects. Herbs, as with other foods, need to be used with wisdom and knowledge and a touch of common sense. The hype that you hear about herbs being unsafe is, almost without exception, the result of two phenomenon:

► The herb was not in its whole form. Someone, in a laboratory setting, broke the herb down into basic compounds, leaving behind the constituents necessary to keep the herb safe. It would be very difficult to take enough fresh lobelia, or even lobelia in a tea or tincture, to dangerously slow your heart because other constituents of lobelia would have you throwing up the excess. Yes, you could slow your heart a little, you might be able to make yourself drowsy and tired, but you could not do yourself any permanent harm.

► The herb reacted with a prescription (or even non-prescription) medication. How does an herb react with a drug? The main factor here is that herbs tend to cleanse and dump poisonous substances from the body. If you are taking blood pressure medication, an herb might cause the liver to dump what it has scooped up from the bloodstream in an attempt to protect you. This may temporarily place too much of the medication back into your bloodstream, artificially dropping your blood pressure to unacceptably low levels, and then leaving you with not enough of the medication in your system later. You can see how this might be annoying if you were relying on, say, your birth control pill. In the case of blood pressure medication it may even be dangerous. The herb is behaving exactly as nature intended it to and it is treating the drug exactly like what it is—a poison!

Herbs can be of value for every body system and cell. Nature has provided us with herbs which benefit the nervous system, immune system, respiratory system, and muscular systems. The properties of each plant target specific areas and functions of the body and accomplish very specific tasks. Modern research has added much knowledge to the literature about the effectiveness of herbs. One area in which the literature is almost silent is the area of what herb to take to deal with the side effects of the use, and misuse, of the huge arsenal of modern drugs. Learning which vitamin or mineral becomes depleted by a certain drug and then supplementing it herbally is the only thing that consistently seems to help.

The following chapters will deal with the separate categories of herbs. I will not attempt to provide an entire picture of each herb in the category, only a few highlights about a few of my favorites. You will have to study a good herb book or two for more information.

©Copyright Butterfly Expressions, llc 2010   Butterfly Miracles with Herbal Remedies

NUTRITIONAL COMPOSITION OF SOME WILD FOOD PLANTS
(Based on appoximately 1 ounce of the fresh plant)

Name	Calories	Protein grams	Fat gr	Calclium mg	Phosphorus mg	Iron mg mg	Potassium I.U.	Vitamin A mg	Thiamine mg	Riboflavin mg	Niacin mg	Vitamin C mg
Alfalfa *Medicago Satvia*	52	6.0	.4	12	5.1	5.4	-	3,410	.13	.14	.5	162
Amaranth *Amaranthas spp*	42	3.7	.8	313	74	5.6	411	1600	.05	.24	1.2	65
Blueberry *Vaccinium spp*	62	.7	.5	15	13	1.0	81	100	.03	.06	.5	14
Burdock *Arctium lappa*	89	2.5	.1	50	58	1.2	180	-	.25	.08	.03	2
Dandelion *Taraxacum off*	45	2.7	.7	187	66	3.1	397	14,000	.19	.26	-	35
Elderberry *Sambuscus can*	72	2.6	.5	38	28	1.6	300	600	.07	.06	.5	36
Horestail *Equisetum arvense*	*20*	*1.0*	*.2*	*58*	*93*	*4.4*	*-*	*180*	*-*	*.07*	*5.6*	*50*
Mallow *Malva spp*	37	4.4	.5	249	69	12.7	-	2,190	.13	.29	1.0	35
Mint *Mentha spp*	32	3.0	.7	194	48	3.8	179	1,296	.13	1.16	.7	64
Nettle *Urtica dicica*	65	5.5	.7	-	-	-	-	6,500	-	-	-	75
Peppergrass *Lepidum spp*	32	2.6	.7	81	75	1.3	606	9,300	.08	.28	1.0	66
Raspberry *Rubus ideas*	73	1.5	1.4	30	22	.9	199	-	.03	.09	.9	18
Shepherds Purse *Capsella burse pastoris*	33	4.2	.5	208	86	4.8	394	1,554	.25	.14	.4	36
Violet *Viola spp*	-	-	-	-	-	-	-	8,200	-	-	-	210
Walnut, Black *Juglens nigra*	626	20.5	59.3	tr	570	6.0	450	300	.22	.1	.7	-
Watercress *Nasturtium off*	19	2.2	.3	151	54	1.7	202	4,900	.08	tr	.9	79
Yucca *Yucca sicifolia*	33	3.1	.2	47	73	.5	-	10	.14	.09	.5	-

Information taken from Mother Earth News #60

©Copyright Butterfly Expressions, llc 2010   Butterfly Miracles with Herbal Remedies

Chapter Four
The Stimulant Herbs

Stimulant herbs help to increase specific actions of the body. They bring up energy levels, increase circulation, increase the pressure and power of the pulse, and because of these actions, aid in the elimination of toxins from the body. There are over 200 herbs listed in this category, most of which are listed in other categories as well. A few of my favorites are: angelica, astragalus, babyberry, capsicum (cayenne), cinnamon, cloves, damiana, echinacea, elder flower, elecampane, ephedra, false unicorn, garlic, gentian, ginger, ginkgo biloba, horseradish, juniper berries, peppermint, rosemary, sage, sarsaparilla, stinging nettles, valerian, and yarrow.

Other valuable stimulant herbs are: blue cohosh, buchu, eucalyptus, ginseng, gravel root, lobelia (treated on its own later and talked about several times already), raspberry, garden sage, shepherd's purse, spikenard.

Butcher's broom is a popular and effective treatment for varicose veins and the heavy, tired, achy feelings in the legs that accompany them. The veins just under the skin of the legs are under a tremendous strain when a person is standing. If a person stands for long periods of time, this pressure can increase ten times over the pressure felt when the person is sitting. Butcher's broom increases circulation, strengthens the veins themselves, and reduces inflammation. One double-blind study was conducted with eighty patients suffering from chronic vein problems in their legs. They had the accompanying symptoms of edema (swelling), burning, tingling, heaviness, and leg cramps. The forty in the group given a butcher's broom preparation showed significant improvement. The improvements were attributed to increased strength and tone of the vein walls. No side effects whatsoever were noted. Butcher's broom can also be used effectively in the treatment of hemorrhoids.

Cayenne is the #1 stimulant herb. It is the purest and most powerful of all the medicinal herbs. The best description I have ever read of cayenne is that it causes "the fires of life to burn more brightly." Cayenne rebuilds (yes, rebuilds) vein structures, removes plaque from veins, and sends the blood rushing along carrying nutrients to every cell of the body. If I could only have one herb in my house, cayenne would be the one that I would choose!

Cayenne's action on the cardiovascular system is almost instantaneous. Cayenne will stop bleeding, even of hemorrhage proportions, and is the first thing that I would reach for at the onset of a stroke or heart attack. Studies have repeatedly shown that cayenne reduces blood cholesterol and triglyceride levels. In addition to that amazing feat, cayenne reduces the instances of platelet aggregation—meaning that cayenne prevents blood clots.

Cayenne contains carotene molecules which are powerful anti-oxidants. Interestingly, although cayenne is hot to the taste it actually lowers body temperatures by stimulating a center in the hypothalamus that is responsible for cooling the body. Cayenne, applied topically, reduces pain.

Cayenne is an accentuator and will increase the healing properties of the other herbs. By adding a touch of cayenne to a respiratory formula, for example, the respiratory herbs will reach the lungs and begin their healing action much more quickly. You will notice in the formulas section of this manual that cayenne, in small parts, is in nearly every formula.

Cayenne is high in zinc, which is essential to the hormonal glands. Cayenne is also high in vitamin A and vitamin C, rutin (which strengthens arteries and veins), iron, calcium, and potassium.

©Copyright Butterfly Expressions, llc 2010   Butterfly Miracles with Herbal Remedies

Echinacea roots, according to modern research, have been found to contain interferon-like properties. Interferon is produced naturally in the body to prevent viral infections and to combat strep and staph bacterias. Echinacea has been used for decades by alternative medicine practitioners in fighting the spread of infectious diseases. It is nice to finally have research to support this. Echinacea is on a par with red clover blossoms as a blood purifier. It should be used in the treatment of chemical toxin poisoning, candida, fungal infections, ulcers, and in clearing the lymph glands.

Echinacea contains a diverse range of active components which affect different aspects of immune function. The Healing Power of Herbs by Michael T. Murray gives an excellent scientific (in layman's terms) treatise on the immune systems various functions and echinacea's impact on them. I like to re-read it from time to time to remind me what a great herb this one is.
Echinacea contains vitamins A, C, and E (this is somewhat unusual in herbs), calcium, iron, iodine (making it a great thyroid herb), potassium, and sulfur. Some herbalists claim that the angustifolia variety is better than purperea (which grows here). I try to use them both in every formula that I make, and prefer them that way.

Elder Flower is a particular favorite for use in acute afflictions such as colds, flu, and hay fever because it *gently* increases blood circulation and promotes sweating. Elder flower is different from cayenne and ginger in that it aids in the detoxification of the body at the cellular level. Elder flower contains constituents known to act as sedatives and pain relievers, yet is an expectorant at the same time. This makes elder flower unique amoung herbs. Usually a sedative, herb or drug, reduces the body's ability to cough and expel mucous from the lungs, etc. Elder flower, combined with oregon grape and yarrow, speeds healing; add mullein to this formula and you have a tremendous healer for lung congestion and asthma.

Elder flower contains large amounts of vitamin A, C and bioflavanoids which protect against germs and viruses.

Ephedra is commonly known as ma huang; a milder version is the Utah plant known as brigham tea. Ma huang contains a constituent known as ephedrine, which has gotten a lot of bad press lately. Some of this bad press is justified in many ways. It must be remembered, however, that herbs taken as teas or tinctured from whole plants do not behave in the same way that commercially prepared plants do. Ephedra, when dried and mashed into a powder and left exposed to light and air, loses some necessary components that have a stabilizing influence on the whole. The bioflavonoids, etc., that are in the whole plant and act as protectors of heart muscle are very fragile. They disappear almost entirely when the herb is processed enough to create a white powder. This is true of several other strong stimulant herbs such as valerian (discussed later in thic chapter). Because some companies attempted to isolate the stimulant and weight loss properties of ma huang, and essentially, created a drug with nasty drug side-effects, ma huang has been removed from the market at the insistence of the FDA.

The removal of ma huang from our herbal repertories is very unfortunate. Ma huang, used after very debilitating illnesses such as pneumonia, stimulates recovery. It helps the body recover from the weakness and fatigue that so often linger after certain types of illnesses.

Ma huang is meant to be used as a short-term stimulant and tonic and used in this way it is perfectly safe. Because of the bad press and the nervousness some people feel, I often use brigham tea, whose action is milder but has, in 250 years of use in Utah, never been linked to any kind of toxicity or side effects. Brigham tea, in the same family, is not illegal—yet—but it is getting difficult to obtain. Many companies will not stock brigham tea at this time because of its family relationship to ma huang. They do not want to come to the attention of government agencies.

©Copyright Butterfly Expressions, llc 2010   Butterfly Miracles with Herbal Remedies

False Unicorn is considered a stimulant herb, although it's primary function seems to be in normalizing the ovaries and the estrogen levels in the body. This herb is commonly used in the prevention of miscarriage (see information with false unicorn/lobelia formula in the recipes section) and in female tonic formulas. False unicorn contains the usual wide range of vitamins and minerals; copper is an unusual component and aids in the uptake of iron.

Ginger is a carrier to the abdominal area, much as cayenne is to the bloodstream. As such, it acts on the stomach, spleen, liver, bladder, and kidneys. Ginger also stimulates the blood, but in a gentler manner.

Ginger acts to lower cholesterol levels by converting cholesterol to bile acids and excreting them from the body. Ginger, while stimulating circulation to an area of the body, also reduces pain sensations. Ginger also prevents ulcer formation in the stomach.

My favorite use for ginger is to place some tincture or powder in the tub at the onset of any bug. Soak for a few minutes, then wrap up warmly. Be very careful not to get chilled after the bath. Stay wrapped until a full sweat is underway, usually about 20 minutes. I have used this method for years to *simulate* and to *stimulate* a fever. The purpose of a fever is to burn off obnoxious little critters and stop an illness such as cold or sore throat right in it's tracks. ***Ginger is high in potassium and contains manganese, silicon, vitamins A, C, B-complex, magnesium, phosphorus, sodium, iron, and zinc.***

Gingko Biloba seems to find its greatest use in arterial circulation, improving electrical transmission in nerves, and in supplying greater amounts of oxygen and nutrition to the brain cells. Ginkgo is one of the true food herbs; its healing effects are slow and steady. Because most people who buy it off the shelf do not understand how this type of herb works, they are disappointed when dramatic improvement does not happen overnight. They do not take it long enough or faithfully enough to reap it's benefits. Bioflavonoids are the key to gingko's usefulness because they protect against free radical damage, aid in enzyme regulation, protect blood vessels and capillaries against plaque buildup, and protect the liver from toxin damage.

Peppermint is another commonly used stimulant herb. Like many other stimulant herbs, peppermint is relaxing in small quantities and stimulating as the dosage or potency is increased. Quietly sipping a small amount of mild peppermint tea calms the nerves and yet peppermint, especially in the essential oil form, is employed by truckers to keep them awake while driving long-haul. Never boil or even overheat this herb when making tea. The medicinal principles are extremely volatile and evaporate easily. Water that is just slightly hotter than luke-warm is ideal for any of the mints.

Peppermint is unique in that it also acts as a nervine in strengthening the heart and digestive systems. Peppermint acts as an anti-spasmodic form of nervine in releasing nerve tension in muscles. Peppermint dulls the hyper-contracting state of the smooth intestinal muscles and is often of benefit in the treatment of irritable bowel syndrome.

Peppermint is high in calcium, magnesium, phosphorus, potassium, sodium, iron, selenium, manganese, vitamin C, silicon ,and zinc.

Stinging Nettle is rarely mentioned in herbal reference materials. It does not seem to have any outstanding medicinal properties other than it's nutritional value. However, it was noted by a friend of mine several years ago that if you combine nettle with kelp and alfalfa, you have most, if not all, of the vitamins and minerals that have been identified as useful to the human body.

©**Copyright Butterfly Expressions, llc 2010   Butterfly Miracles with Herbal Remedies**

Nettle is so rich in iron and vitamin K that you can almost feel it thickening the blood.   It contains almost none, or just negligible amounts of the usual vitamins found in herbs, but the vitamin A content is off the charts.   Nettle is right up there with huge servings of carrots eaten raw. Stinging nettle even contains a very absorbable protein and some fats. A wonderful food herb!!

Valerian is usually thought of as a sedative herb by most people. Valerian's main impact is on the nerves, brain, liver, and heart. Because it heals and rebuilds in these areas, people feel calmed, strengthened, and uplifted by this herb. This is one of the best herbs in the world for helping people sleep and helping them cope with high levels of stress. Valerian contains large amounts of calcium and comes with its own supply of magnesium so the calcium is readily absorbed and made available to build bones, strengthen nerves, and relax the smooth muscles.

It might be advisable to use valerian in a small quantity the first time with each person. Valerian is one of the few herbs that I have seen people react negatively to. I suspect that the large amounts of calcium (which toxins love to hook to in order to leave the body) cause the body to cleanse and are responsible for this effect. In a few people, valerian—whether fresh, dried, or tinctured—produces exactly the opposite of the usual calming effect. In fact, for these people, valerian is an irritating sort of stimulant, similar to but stronger than caffeine. These people become nervous, irritable, and restless until the herb is metabolized and passed from their systems. Ocassionally, the reaction will be extreme fatigue and lethargy. Some herbal references tell you that this effect is more pronounced when using the dried form of the herb. For that reason I always wildcraft my own and process it fresh, but I have seen some people react to the valerian when harvesting it in the wild. More information on valerian is provided on page 44 in the chapter on alterative and adaptogenic herbs.

Yarrow The herbs that I have included here in the stimulant section were chosen because they are the ones that I use and am most familiar with. Of course, any herb on the list at the end of this section would be of great benefit.   While definitely a stimulant herb, it also has some unique characteristics that set it apart from the rest of this class. Yarrow contains all the usual vitamins and minerals found in plants used medicinally but it also contains vitamin F, an essential fatty acid necessary for the good health of all body membranes, including those surrounding the brain and the brain itself. Also, because of the vitamin F content, yarrow is considered an astringent herb (one of the best), which means that it contracts and tightens membranes making the retention of gallstones or kidney stones, etc., impossible. Yarrow can be used for any condition in which too much secretion (mucous, etc.) is a problem. Vitamin F is the basis for the production of the hormone like prostaglandins produced in the cells and is partially responsible for yarrow's ability to seal and heal wounds. Placing the fresh leaves on a wound or deep cut will heal and seal the tissues together almost immediately and in an almost miraculous fashion.

Besides being considered a stimulant, an astringent, a nutritive, a diuretic, an anthilitic, a carminative, and a digestive, yarrow is one of the best diaphoretic/febrifuge herbs available. Add to that yarrow's ability to pull the edges of wounds together and you have one amazing herb! I have always been doubtful of herbs that claim to do everything, but I have used yarrow for something in every one of the categories listed above over the years. This herb really works!

Yarrow contains vitamins A, C, E, and F and some vitamin K. It also contains manganese, copper, potassium, iodine, and iron.

©**Copyright Butterfly Expressions, llc 2010   Butterfly Miracles with Herbal Remedies**

Chapter Five
Tonic Herbs

Tonic herbs are used to increase energy, vigor and strength by nourishing the body. There are tonic herbs for the liver, heart, nerves, and for every organ and system of the body. Most tonic herbs, no matter what category they are predominantly listed in, strengthen the digestive system in some way. The result of this is an increase in the assimilation of nutrients The nutrients then feed and strengthen the body where they are most needed and most appropriate.

Tonic herbs also cleanse the organs and tissues of the heavy mucous which is too often found covering the membranes. Excessive mucous clogs the channels of elimination and absorption in individual cells and in entire body systems and organs. These herbs help re-establish and maintain normal tension and tone in cells, fibers, and tissues. They sharpen the appetite and gradually bring the person to a state of greater strength, energy, and vitality.

Most tonic herbs have a bitter taste. They are used primarily in convalescence from disease or illness, or at other times when the body is in a run-down condition. This is unfortunate. If these herbs were a regular part of our lives, we would be much stronger, more vital and active, and much more resistant to disease.

These herbs were valued as spring tonics in the previous century. Fatigue and a general run-down condition was often experienced by people as a result of a diet lacking in fruits and vegetables during the winter months.

There are about 3000 herbs listed in the pharmacopoeias of the world; about 1000 of which are used by traditional herbalists (chosen because they are non-poisonous and completely safe). Of these 1000 approximately 350 are listed as tonic. Develop your own pets. It is not necessary to understand them all. It is far better to use a few herbs, chosen for their effects in different areas, with confidence and acumen than to dabble in a whole range using none of them very effectively.

I will attempt to divide the tonic herbs according to the area of the body that they address most strongly. You will probably notice that some herbs appear in more than one category. Herbs are still just as God created them; they have not been broken apart by chemical means in a laboratory. They are able to address the entire person, not just a specific area or system. Please remember too, that herbs return the body to stasis—a static state or balanced way of being. Put simply, this means that the same herb or herbal combination that will lower high blood pressure will raise low blood pressure. This will be done according to the needs of the body. Herbs also contain their own balancing agents to prevent over-doses or side effects. These facts make the categorization of herbs according to body system a little bit artificial. Nevertheless, certain herbs do have an affinity for particular areas of the body and lists such as this can be helpful in finding them when you need them. This affinity for particular body systems is especially true of the tonic and nervine herbs.

This chapter will explain in more detail a few of the general systemic tonics. It will also give a more detailed description of a few herbs from specific categories such as diuretics, astringents, etc., that I am particularly fond of. An index is provided at the back of the book to help you locate these descriptions as you have a need for them.

©Copyright Butterfly Expressions, llc 2010   Butterfly Miracles with Herbal Remedies

General Tonics: agrimony, alfalfa, brigham tea, comfrey, dulce, echinacea, elethero, dulce, ginseng, licorice, nettles, sarsaparilla, slippery elm, yucca

Nerve Tonics (nervines): black cohosh, catnip, chamomile, hops, lady slipper, lobelia, motherwort, passion flower, peppermint, skullcap, St. John's wort, squawvine, valerian

Cirulatory Tonics (including veins and arteries): angelica, butcher's broom, cayenne, devil's claw, ginger, garlic, gingko biloba, hawthorne, horseradish, mistletoe, saw palmetto (prostate), turmeric, wood betony, yarrow

Heart Tonics (cardiac): angelica, astragalus, comfrey, dong quai, ginseng, gingko biloba, hawthorne, marshmallow, motherwort, mullein, passion flower, rehemannia, yucca

Digestive Tonics (stomachics, bitters): agrimony, angelica, aniseed, barberry, cascara sagrada, catnip, chamomile, clove, comfrey, dandelion, elecampane, fennel, fenugreek, garlic, gentian, milk thistle, peppermint, stone root, turmeric, uva ursi

Urinary Tonics (diuretics): buchu, corn silk, cranberries, golden rod, gravel root, horsetail, marshmallow, parsley root, rehamannia, squawvine, stoneroot

Liver Tonics (hepatics): dandelion, milk thistle, sassafras, stoneroot, cascara sagrada

Biliary Tonics (stimulates bile): dandelion, goldenseal, oregon grape root, parsley, turkey rhubarb, wild yam, yarrow

Hormonal Tonics (hormones and sexual function): blessed thistle, blue cohosh, burdock, chaste tree, damiana, dong quai, false unicorn, licorice, milk thistle, raspberry, thimble berry, uva ursi

Respiratory Tonics: angelica, aniseed, bee pollen, coltsfoot, elecampane, garlic, horehound, mullein

Immune Tonics (adaptogenic/alterative): bee pollen, echinacea, garlic, ginger, ginseng, elethero, goldenseal, licorice

Brain Tonics: Gingko Biloba, Gota Kola

Agrimony was used by the native Americans as a tonic tea to strengthen the whole system. Agrimony is used to treat urinary infections. It should be taken between acute bouts to strengthen the urinary tract until repeated infections are no longer a problem. Agrimony is also used for strengthening the digestive system; it is of benefit to the stomach, intestines, liver, and gallbladder.

Agrimony has strong astringent qualities. It is useful whenever bleeding is present and is sometimes used for bleeding and discharges associated with menopause. Ointments made with agrimony and yarrow as key ingredients are used to treat hemorrhoids.

Agrimony is said to have antviral properties and to promote the healing of wounds and sores. It is excellent applied topically to venomous bites and stings, and can be taken internally at the same time for this. Agrimony should be used cautiously if the person is already suffering from dryness of bodily secretions.

©Copyright Butterfly Expressions, llc 2010   Butterfly Miracles with Herbal Remedies

Alfalfa has been in use as a "miracle herb" for centuries; the Arabs call it the "Father of Herbs." Alfalfa contains the widest variety of vitamins and minerals of any other food on earth. With high levels of chlorophyll, it is thought to be perfectly balanced for complete absorption in the body. Alfalfa is very high in vitamin K. Vitamin K is the blood clotting vitamin and is also linked to the prevention of osteoporosis.

Another unique nutritional factor of alfalfa is that it contains eight of the essential amino acids and is rich in protein. It is somewhat unusual to find protein in plants. There is quite a bit of protein in alfalfa and it is in a form that the body uptakes readily. The protein in alfalfa makes it a very useful herb. An attempt to list even the most recent studies and all of the things that alfalfa is traditionally used for would be ludicrously lengthy. Just remember—and use frequently—this valuable, nutritious herb.

Angelica is another systemic tonic. It is useful in so many areas in the body, and in so many ways, that it is difficult to choose which category it would be most important to mention it in. Angelica is used to improve circulation. It is a good herb to use regularly in the winter as it warms the body. Because of its warming properties, angelica is good for spasms in the stomach or intestinal tract. Applied topically, angelica eases the pain of arthritis and muscles spasms. Angelica is often used in the treatment of colds, coughs, bronchitis, pneumonia, flus, and fevers. Angelica is an excellent expectorant.

Angelica is an outstanding emmenagogue—promotes normal menstrual flow. Angelica's ability to strip the endometrial lining is so pronounced that it should be avoided by pregnant women. In fact, I have often used angelica, in both herbal and essential oil form, after a birth when the placenta is not detaching properly. It works every time. Several properties of angelica probably combine to make this happen. Angelica, as mentioned previously, works on the circulation but angelica also has hormone balancing properties. It is used, both internally and applied to the breasts when any lump first appears. If the lump, cancerous or otherwise, is related to high estrogen levels, angelica will rapidly dissolve it and lower the estrogen levels in the blood. A program including estrogen should be followed for several weeks to stabilize the estrogen and other hormone levels.

Angelica should be used cautiously by diabetics; it has a reputation for slightly raising blood sugar levels.

Bee pollen Bee pollen is usually referred to as a complete or perfect food. It contains more than 96 different identified nutrients, including everything that is known to be necessary to sustain life and achieve optimum health. The nutrients in bee pollen include 22 amino acids, all of the identified vitamins, folic acid, polyunsaturated fatty acids, enzymes, and the trace minerals that have been identified as essential to the body. Some of these nutrients and trace minerals are very important and several of them are not manufactured by the body. Among the nutrients in bee pollen are all of the major anti-oxidants that have been identified by science so far. Bee pollen is approximately 40% protein. These proteins are readily absorbed by the body without the need for a lot of further metabolizing.

Well nourished bodies cope more easily with stress, are more resistant to disease, have few allergies, and enjoy increased levels of energy, stamina, and endurance.

As a much younger woman, I took bee pollen during the winter every year for several years. I had been told that doing so would make the upcoming spring allergy season much easier to bear. I found that to be true. There was a ***very*** noticeable difference—for the worse—in the years that I forgot. Eventually, with liver cleansing and other things in addition to the bee pollen, my many allergies have been almost completely eliminated. I no longer think in terms of "allergy seasons" and I have only one or two minor food allergies left.

©Copyright Butterfly Expressions, llc 2010   **Butterfly Miracles with Herbal Remedies**

Scientists have tried to create a synthetic form of bee pollen. While the synthetic product seems to be identical in components and molecular structure to natural bee pollen, when it was fed to worker bees, the bees die within a week. **Synthetic nutrients do not nourish.** *Only God can make a tree.*

Blessed Thistle is one of nature's best hormone balancing herbals. Often thought of in connection with nursing mothers, it is also useful for most types of menstrual difficulties. The bitters in blessed thistle aid the digestive tracts and are known to have antimicrobial activity. Blessed thistle strengthens the immune system and hinders the formation of abnormal cells. This makes it potentially useful for people with cancer and in the prevention of the growth of scar tissue.

Cascara Sagrada was admitted to the *U.S. Pharmacopoeia* in 1877 and is still included as an official medicine. Cascara Sagrada is known throughout the world for its benefits to the muscular activity of the colon. Restores natural bowel function without cramping and is not habit-forming; it does not make the colon dependent as do many other laxatives. Cascara contains significant amounts of calcium, B-complex vitamins, potassium, phosphorus, selenium, vitamin A, sodium, chlorine (in the natural and usable state that the body requires a small amount of), magnesium, iron, niacin, and trace amounts of manganese, silicon, and vitamin C.

Chamomile has become so well-known for its ability as a safe and mild sedative to induce sleep or relaxation that many of its other properties are frequently overlooked. The tonic and sedative properties (tryptophan constituents) of chamomile make it an excellent choice for ulcers and indigestion. I particularly love this herb for babies and small children for colic, upset tummy, and nightmares. I blend it with catnip in a glycerine based tincture, making it mild enough for even the tiniest patient. Contains, among its many other blessings, a high level of silicon and selenium.

This herb has a strong anti-histiminic effect and is a gentle liver cleanser and hormone balancer. Chamomile is often used to relieve nausea and morning sickness during pregnancy. Chamomile regulates peristalsis activity and is used to treat both diarrhea and constipation, illustrating once again the action of herb in bringing that body back into a balanced state.

False Unicorn is one of the best and most positive tonic and stimulant herbs for the reproductive systems of both male and female. Most people associate this herb with the prevention of miscarriage, and where the corpus luteum is slow to sluff off so implantation of the egg can take place, false unicorn works wonders. This herb is so mild that it is often well received by the stomach where everything else is being rejected. This herb is as good as any vermifuge (ridding the body of parasites) but is much milder. It is also becoming quite endangered and is ridiculously expensive.

Garlic Garlic has been used for a long list of medicinal purposes for a long, long time. It is considered by many alternative practitioners to be nature's most effective antibiotic. In the United States, garlic consistently ranks among the top five best-selling herbs. Until recently, most of the benefits of garlic have been considered folklore based on unreliable anecdotal experiences. In November of 1990 a report in the Journal of the American Medical Association claimed the therapeutic roles of garlic have been described in more than 1,000 scientific studies. Some of these studies were quoted and explained in the article. Some of the health benefits shown by these studies were that garlic can lower cholesterol levels, prevent blood clots from forming, strengthen veins and arteries, reduce blood pressure, protect against bacterial and fungal infections, and even prevent cancer. The best article on the benefits of garlic that I have seen in recent years is found at www.thenutritionreporter.com/garlic.html.

©**Copyright Butterfly Expressions, llc 2010   Butterfly Miracles with Herbal Remedies**

Hawthorne and other flavonoid-rich compounds such as blueberries, bilberries, and grapes are valued for several unique reasons. These herbs have very strong intra-cellular strengthening capabilities as well as significant collagen-stabilizing actions. Collagen is the abundant protein that makes up the cytoplasm of cells and maintains cellular integrity. The weakness or destruction of collagen lies at the heart of many diseases and debilitating conditions. Hawthorne flavonoids also stabilize vitamin C, protecting it from destruction or oxidation. Hawthorne greatly decreases capillary permeability and fragility. Hawthorne has been clinically proven effective in reducing blood pressure, angina attacks, serum cholesterol levels, and the deposits of cholesterol along arterial walls. Hawthorne's ability to dilate coronary blood vessels has been repeatedly demonstrated in clinical trials.

Horsetail (also known as shavegrass) is most noted for its silicon content, which is very high. Recent studies in Europe have found that broken bones do not heal well, even in the presence of high levels of calcium, if there is insufficient amounts of silicon available in the blood. This interaction between calcium and silicon makes this herb valuable to strengthen hair and nails and to prevent the formation of gallstones and kidney stones. There are many great diuretic herbs, but none with the other benefits of horsetail. Horsetail is also high in vitamin E and selenium, and is certainly much cheaper than taking a supplement of vitamin E.

Myrrh has been recommended as a substitute for goldenseal, but I can find nothing in its constituents that would indicate this as a good idea. I frequently add a little myrrh to a formula because it contains a compound known as silymarin, which protects the liver from chemical toxins. Myrrh is a powerful antiseptic with a special affinity for the mucous membranes and gives vitality and strength to the digestive system. Myrrh aids in the balance of acid and alkaline in the blood.

Oregon Grape   The plants goldenseal, barberry, and oregon grape share similar indications and effects because of their high content of berberis alkaloids. Goldenseal has a great reputation throughout the herbal world, but according to spectrographic analysis, oregon grape has every attribute of goldenseal. Oregon grape has additional properties shown to be beneficial in the treatment of a variety of skin conditions.

I have found through years of herbal use that local herbs work better for local people; I use very few Chinese herbs because there is usually something just as effective that grows here in our mountains and works even better for my friends and family. Oregon grape is a shining example of this principle. I use it almost everywhere that I previously used goldenseal, and with excellent results. Oregon grape is much less expensive (free if you wildcraft it). It has become a mainstay of my herbal repertory.

The following information has been taken from the book The Healing Power of Herbs by Michael T. Murray. This book is more scientific than anecdotal and provides a lot of good information about the clinically proven, medicinal properties of a few good herbs, including the berberine producing varieties. Everything said here can be applied equally to goldenseal and oregon grape root.

Perhaps the most exciting, and most used effect of these herbs is their broad spectrum of antibiotic activity. Their action against a wide variety of pathogens is actually stronger than that of antibiotics commonly used in the medical world, but they produce none of the side effects of prescription antibiotics (such as the overgrowth of candida that is a common side effect of prescription antibiotic use).

©**Copyright Butterfly Expressions, llc 2010   Butterfly Miracles with Herbal Remedies**

Another effect of berberine producing plants is their ability to inhibit the adherence of strep and staph bacteria to their host cells. In other words, the critters that aren't killed outright are flushed from the system because they are unable to cling to the cells of the body. This work is accomplished at very low doses and with **no side effects.   Don't forget these two herbs in the treatment of strep throat and staph infections and any infection of the eye.**

Other places where clinical trials are rapidly establishing a reputation for berberine containing plants is in the treatment of liver disorders, various cancers, and in the treatment of conditions involving depressed white blood cell counts. This includes white blood cell counts which have been reduced by chemotherapy treatments. Goldenseal and oregon grape are often used as a tonic to boost a sluggish glandular system and to promote balanced hormonal activity.

Goldenseal sometimes has a negative impact on blood sugar levels in diabetics. This quirk is not a part of the action of oregon grape.

Dosage: generally non-toxic but it should be remembered that low doses of these herbs are very effective. Higher doses are not recommended for pregnancy and may interfere with the metabolism of vitamin B. **Higher doses are not more effective; more is not always better!**

Saw palmetto The primary use of saw palmetto has always been in the treatment of enlarged prostate and the accompanying urinary disorders. Saw palmetto has repeatedly shown excellent results in double-blind, placebo-controlled clinical trials, but the most interesting results I have seen were in a multi-center study conducted in 1994. This study is quoted in Michael T. Murray's book <u>The Healing Power of Herbs</u>.

While results for urine flow, residual urine amounts, and prostate enlargement were impressive, it was the results in the quality-of-life portion of the tests that I found impressive. There were a total of 350 men in this study. They were asked, on day one and day 90, to choose one of seven terms that best described themselves.   The results were as follows:

Day 0		Day 90
2.3%	Happy	24.0%
.6%	Delighted	5.4%
9.7%	Satisfied	36.8%
22.7%	Mitigated	20.9%
43.8%	Unsatisfied	9.5%
18.5%	Unhappy	2.4%
2.3%	Hopeless	1.0%

Saw palmetto is completely safe. No significant side effects have ever been reported in any clinical trial.

Ginger and **Peppermint** are two of the best tonic herbs. They are discussed in some detail in the previous chapter, as is **Gingko Biloba**, so they will not be discussed here.

©**Copyright Butterfly Expressions, llc 2010   Butterfly Miracles with Herbal Remedies**

Chapter Six
Lobelia—In a Class By Itself

Lobelia is one of the greatest herbs that we have available to us. It was discovered by the great 19th century herbalist, Dr. Samuel Thompsen. He was a contemporary of Joseph Smith and believed by Jospeh Smith to be an inspired man. Dr. Thompsen said,

> "There is no vegetable which the earth produces more harmless in its effect on the human system and none more powerful in removing disease and promoting health. . . It is calculated to remove the cause, and no more, as food removes hunger, and drink thirst. It clears all obstructions to the extremities, without regard to the names of disease, until it produces an equilibrium throughout the system, and will be felt in the fingers and toes, producing a prickling feeling like that caused by a knock on the elbow. This symptom is alarming to those unacquainted with its operation, but is always favorable, being certain indication of the turn of the disorder, and patients generally gain from that time. . .This plant is the most important article I make use of in my practice."

In 1809, in the midst of much persecution of naturopathic practitioners by the allopathic doctors of the day, Dr. Thompsen was brought to trial for the use of lobelia. Much vituperative press accompanied this trial and has been quoted and then quoted again over the years for many of the same reasons as the original statements were written. Without going into great detail, let it be sufficient to say that Dr. Thompsen was acquitted and the court record shows that no case could be made for the administration of lobelia sensibly as being a harmful agent. The very fact that so much continual misrepresentation abounds concerning this herb indicates to me that it must be very valuable indeed in curing illness.

Lobelia is, as far as I know, the strongest relaxant and sedative herb known anywhere. As indicated, there are some who claim that it is a dangerous herb. I certainly would not describe it as dangerous in the sense of life-threatening, but it would be an easy herb to overuse and abuse. Lobelia is strongly emetic, so even though it probably could relax and sedate the respiratory system to the point of death, you would have a very difficult time keeping enough of it down to seriously harm yourself! You might, however, feel like death would be a welcome relief from the vomiting and cramping!!

Lobelia can remove obstructions and congestions throughout the body and in the blood at a rapid and remarkable rate. An overdose produces the very strong response of vomiting and diarrhea. The vomiting and diarrhea are brought about because the eliminative organs cannot keep up with the housecleaning that the lobelia has set into motion.   Lobelia is a vasodilator and a muscle relaxant. Coupled with the vomiting these sensations can be really alarming! But, even in an overdose situation, the marvelous cleansing that has resulted eventually leaves the person feeling wonderful—energetic and relaxed at the same time. It takes a very large amount of lobelia to produce these symptoms. It is not something you need to be concerned about. If you take a bit too much, you body will respond with a slightly chilly sensation. This early warning signal can be trusted and passes in just a few moments.

Lobelia is the most efficient of the herbs that act as carriers for other herbs. Lobelia added to any combination will deliver the herb quickly and efficiently to the area of distress. Moreover, it seems to be selective in its course of action. Dr. Christopher often described, in his talks and lectures, the cases of two young men who were similar in age but completely different in strength and constitution. Each young man had a boil forming on his neck. The same formula, with a bit of lobelia added, was administered to both. The strong, robust young man with a good digestion and elimination system was healed by the boil disappearing into the body and the poisons being carried off by his system. The other young man, very weak and delicate, was healed by the boil continuing to encapsulate and grow on his neck until it could be safely removed; his system did not have the strength to process the toxins internally. Because of the intelligence of the lobelia the best action for the circumstances was chosen by the body. Dr. Christopher referred to lobelia as the thinking herb. I have personally witnessed this aspect of the action of lobelia.

Because lobelia is such a strong relaxant I never give it, especially to small children, without a baseline pulse rate being established. This enables me to ascertain how much the pulse is slowing, if at all. This does not have to be an exact count, only a feel for what is going on. In sick children the pulse is usually racing and thready and the slowing brought on by the lobelia is actually a beneficial effect.

Lobelia is usually administered as part of a formula, rather than by itself. When used as a small percentage of a formula, it is possible to get all of the beneficial effects of lobelia and never have to give a thought to possible over-dose.

If I am dealing with a child whose pulse is not racing or with a particularly debilitated adult, I will administer a stimulant such as cayenne, ginger, or peppermint prior to, or along with, the lobelia. This is not difficult since peppermint tea is probably indicated anyway and it takes only a swallow or two of tea to offset the sedative effects of the lobelia. Formulas containing lobelia already have a mild stimulant added into the recipe in most cases.

Some Basics About the Use of Lobelia

In childbirth, lobelia is often administered with cayenne as a means of relaxing the pelvic muscles. I have found that this gently speeds labor along. The increased circulation produced by the lobelia and cayenne helps in producing a very pink, well-oxygenated child and in keeping the mother from tearing.

BBL—the recipe is given in the tinctures section—has so many uses that, try as I might, I will probably not get them all listed. In this formula, lobelia is combined with blue vervain, blue cohosh, black cohosh, and skullcap to produce an antispasmodic formula. This means that BBL will provide relief from anything that manifests with spasms or pain with a pulsing quality. Examples might be coughing, muscle or abdominal cramping, or any kind of pain that pulses—such as toothache, earache, certain types of stomach ache, pleurisy, boils, etc.

BBL can be taken internally and applied topically as a liniment for muscle cramps. Topical application does not require the giving of a stimulant. In fact, when BBL for its relaxant properties, stimulant herbs such as cayenne, ginger, or peppermint should not be used.

I put a few drops of BBL, along with mullein or garlic oil, in the ear for earache. The BBL acts as a pain reliever while carrying the medicinal properties of the oil more deeply and more rapidly. The addition of BBL increases the antibacterial action of the garlic or mullein oils.

©Copyright Butterfly Expressions, llc 2010   Butterfly Miracles with Herbal Remedies

A couple of dropperfuls of BBL in a tub of warm water relieves cramps, including really nasty menstrual ones. Taking it by mouth at the same time is also helpful. Used as a liniment on the abdomen, or on any muscle that is cramping, it brings almost instant relief.

I smashed the index finger on my right hand thoroughly one day and the pain was excruciating. I put arnica oil on it—for the swelling. I poured some BBL tincture into a small paper cup and put my finger in it. The pain was manageable that way and within a few hours most of the discoloration, swelling, and pain were gone. I even managed to make a fist and go back to foot zoning within a few days.

A few drops of BBL should always be considered for convulsions in children. Try to remember that, if you can. I have frequently forgotten. When working with children I usually use the BBL that is made with a glycerine base rather than alcohol. The alcohol formula is best for use in the tub, although you can use the glycerite. The glycerite leaves just a little bit of a sticky feeling on the skin after the bath. For convulsions—and the prevention of convulsions during a fever—I use a few drops of glycerine BBL by mouth and a bath in luke-warm water at the same time.

BBL is also excellent for the treatment of asthma—both as a way of dealing with an attack and as part of a long-term, overall program. Lobelia, added to any respiratory formula, will facilitate the clearing of the passages.

I have used elder flower to which a bit of lobelia has been added to reduce a fever. It is always very effective.

*** *Please note the number of times lobelia, in a small amount, has been added to the tincture recipes found later in this booklet.****

Dosage: Lobelia should be given in small doses for healing purposes, and in larger doses when its emetic or cleansing properties are required.   A stimulant, such as cayenne, peppermint, or ginger should be considered unless extreme relaxation is required.

©Copyright Butterfly Expressions, llc 2010   Butterfly Miracles with Herbal Remedies

Chapter Seven
Diuretics and Nephritic Herbs
(with Anthilitic and Lithotriptic Herbs—a subcategory)

The function of the kidneys is best described as filters for the blood. Your blood flows constantly through your kidneys to be purified or filtered. If the kidneys fail to accomplish their job, the result is a toxic system. This leads to depression, fatigue, restless sleep, pains in the back, headache, achy joints, memory loss, and irritability. Many chronic diseases such as Multiple Sclerosis and Parkinson's are made worse by unsupported and failing kidneys. The diuretic herbs can make a significant difference in the progress of these conditions.

The diuretic herbs are used to increase the flow of urine and to relieve the cells and tissues of excess water and uric acid. The word diuretic usually denotes a simple dumping of liquid from the bladder, kidneys, and tissues. It is almost always advisable to include herbs that heal and strengthen these organs at the same time. These herbs are sometimes referred to as nephritic herbs, although many herbal references simply lump these two categories together.

Diaphoretic and nephritic herbs are among the most important herbs you will ever use. Many diseases defined today by modern medicine have an underlying component of the kidneys inefficiently functioning, allowing uric acid crystals to form in the brain, along the nerve endings, under the skin, and along the long muscles. This buildup can cause excruciating pain and even death. Add to that the embarrassment of bed-wetting or incontinence and there is considerable motivation to learn to use herbal diuretics well. It should be noted that both bed-wetting and incontinence usually have nerve destruction—often from years of uric acid crystal accumulation—that also need to be addressed with mild herbal nervines.

There are over 450 known herbs which have diuretic properties. Listed among them are: **alfalfa, brigham tea, buchu, corn silk, dandelion, hawthorne, horsetail, juniper berries, marshmallow, motherwort, mullein, nettle, parsley,** and **uva ursi**.

Alfalfa would be an excellent choice for a diuretic if anemia or any borderline vitamin and mineral deficiencies exist. Alfalfa contains a very wide range of nutrients. As mentioned in chapter 5, alfalfa is a very nourishing herb. Alfalfa is often recommended when a regimen of sulfa drugs or antibiotics has been followed.

Buchu Buchu has a long history of use in herbal formulas for kidney, bladder, prostate, and menstrual problems. The diuretic properties of buchu are quite mild but unique. It is best used in conjunction with other appropriate remedies. Mixed with marshmallow and mullein, buchu is an effective remedy for gout. Buchu is said to be a mild uterine stimulant. As such it should probably be avoided during pregnancy.

Dandelion would be the herb of choice—or should be added to a formula—if a mild liver cleanse would be beneficial. Dandelion is particularly effective when the stress to the kidneys is related to chemical or toxic metal poisoning or detoxification. Dandelion acts in the capacity of a blood cleanser as well as a diuretic. Dandelion removes obstructions from the liver, spleen, pancreas, gallbladder, bladder, and kidneys, making it a very useful herb. Dandelion is very high in vitamin A. For a list of vitamin A deficiency ailments, see page 11. Dandelion leaves have a mild and pleasant taste in the early spring but become quite bitter as the summer progresses. In the winter, the medicinal properties pull back into the root and the root is the part of the plant that should be used then. The root is the part that is commercially marketed for medicinal purposes.

©Copyright Butterfly Expressions, llc 2010   Butterfly Miracles with Herbal Remedies

Horsetail, which was discussed in some detail in the previous chapter, is probably my all time favorite basic diuretic. Horsetail grows profusely in this valley and is a strange herb in that it has male and female variety. The two forms always grow in proximity to each other and are both equally useful. The male version grows tall and straight and is usually referred to as joint grass; the female version is bushier, although the center stem looks much like the male joint grass version. The bushy female kind is referred to as foxtail, for obvious reasons.

Horsetail temporarily increases the acidity of the urine. This is unusual in herbal remedies, but part of horsetail's effectiveness is because the increased acidity kills any bacteria in the kidneys and bladder. Horsetail also stimulates the coagulation of the blood, curtailing excessive bleeding. This herb is especially useful for menstruation that is too profuse or for the bleeding that sometimes accompanies the passage of kidney stones and gravel.

Horsetail contains silica, making it a good herb for strengthening bones, hair, and nails. Horsetail is best taken in frequent small doses, and unless mixed with a demulcent herb, for only short periods of time. Because of the acidity factor mentioned above, horsetail taken in large quantities for long periods of time can become irritating to tender mucous membranes.

Juniper berries are a stimulating diuretic herb. They are beneficial in formulas for urine retention in the bladder, gravel in the kidneys, and uric acid toxicity. Caution with juniper berries is advised during pregnancy as it is a mild uterine stimulant. Juniper berries should be taken for a short period of time— or in conjunction with demulcent or nephritic herbals. Juniper berries can be caustic and irritating by themselves or when taken for too long a time.

Researchers into the medicinal properties of herbs rely to a great degree on folklore and anecdotal evidence because, too often, no studies have been done using the herbs in "whole" form (not broken down into components in a laboratory setting). Researchers pay particularly close attention to overlapping traditions—in other words, uses for an herb that are the same among American Indian tribes, traditional wise women in Europe, Chinese/Eastern practitioners, and monks in Tibet. This overlapping gives credence to the use of an herb for a particular thing.

It seems that here in the western part of the world we have no problem with this method of "proof" as long as what is being "proved" is very material in nature. As Michael Moore says it in his book Herbs or the Mountain West, "

> If unrelated traditions say that yarrow clots blood, it is easy to admit that such is probably the case; if they say that Juniper clears "bad vibes," many of us will back off and start to twitch skeptically."

Healing philosophies in other parts of the world have for generations factored in the emotional and mental state of a person when looking for a remedy that will help. They also pay close attention to the effects of herbal remedies on their clientele. Here in the west we are *finally* beginning to embrace this understanding. Information is becoming available about the emotional/mental picture of plants. While this book is materialistic and nutritional in its focus, a study of plants as essential oils can broaden your understanding a great deal. It seems to be an accepted thing that essential oils can help us change our emotional response to our world and much has been written on that subject (even by me). I would recommend that you broaden your education along those lines and beyond the scope of this booklet .

©**Copyright Butterfly Expressions, llc 2010   Butterfly Miracles with Herbal Remedies**

Marshmallow is both a diuretic and a demulcent. It soothes the inflamed tissues of the urinary tract while it acts against urine retention. I often use marshmallow simply because no matter who calls, from where, they can usually go into their backyard or garden and find enough marshmallow plants to set them to rights. Even in winter, if you can get to any of the root, you will have an excellent remedy. I have given this advice to many people who call me in pain with a gout in their toes. (I have used it myself in the past for this reason more than once!)

Marshmallow (or just mallow, as it is often referred to) is very soothing to sore throats when sipped as a warm tea. Mallow tea is also useful for indigestion and sensitive stomach. Mallow can be added to poultices to reduce inflammation and lessen muscular pain. The tea is used among the Indian people of New Mexico as a wash for inflamed skin, especially with infants.

Mullein is only mildly diuretic. I have placed it here because it is almost always added to kidney/bladder formulas because it is anti-inflammatory and soothing. Mullein is a demulcent herb without peer or competition, except possibly by slippery elm. I like to add mullein to any diuretic formula that is going to be used for more than a few days because it protects the urinary tissues. Diuretics can be a little bit caustic, acidic, and drying to these delicate tissues in order to accomplish their purpose. Mullein offsets these aspects without interfering with the diuretic and antibacterial properties of the herbs or herbal formulas. Mullein will be discussed in much greater detail in chapter nine.

Parsley root is more than just a kidney/bladder herb. It is specific to the adrenal glands and helpful in formulas for the removal of both gallstones and kidney stone. Parsley has properties that powerfully benefit the optic nerves, the nerves in the brain, and the entire sympathetic nervous system. Parsley is rich in vitamins and minerals and contains a lot of easily assimilated iron. Parsley contains whopping amounts of vitamins A, B, and C. The B vitamins alone make it worthwhile to add to your food recipes and to use frequently as a medicinal herb.

While parsley is an excellent herb, it should be avoided by nursing mothers as it efficiently dries up the milk supply.

Fresh parsley tea was a mainstay for one woman (very close to me) who had a rare and nasty cancer of the blood. Doctors were continually amazed at the healthy functioning of her kidneys. She lived many years beyond their original predictions—with an impressively good quality of life for most of those years. I personally attribute much of this to the strength of the kidneys from the consumption of so much parsley tea.

Squawvine (also known as partridge berry) is used in the treatment of water retention, kidney/bladder gravel and stones, and for relieving the pain of backaches caused by an irritated urinary tract. Squawvine is used particularly by women as it tones and strengthens the uterine and pelvic muscles. Squawvine prepares these muscles for the processes of labor and birth.

A formula containing cramp bark, raspberry leaves, false unicorn, and a small part of lobelia is often effective to prevent miscarriage, particularly in the early months. Squawvine is a mild nervine so its use during a threatened miscarriage has two-fold benefits. This herb also helps to regulate the bowels and improve appetite and digestion. I have used just false unicorn and lobelia with success in miscarriage for many years as a midwife. (See CB formula for a similar recipe)

©Copyright Butterfly Expressions, llc 2010   Butterfly Miracles with Herbal Remedies

Stoneroot is combined with gravel root and diuretic herbs for the removal of bladder and kidney stones. Stoneroot will gradually dissolve kidney stones, but the stones must be kept up out of the ducts until they are small enough to pass more easily. Sipping lemon juice and lying on the back with the feet elevated from time to time throughout the day will usually accomplish this. Persistence with this regimen can save you much pain and an expensive kidney stone removal procedure. Stoneroot taken along with mild demulcents for a few weeks once or twice a year may prevent the formation of kidney stones at all in the future.

In addition, stoneroot's astringent properties restore the tone of flaccid veins. This makes it an outstanding remedy for varicose veins and hemorrhoids. It should be taken internally, and where possible, applied externally also. Stoneroot is also used in the treatment of constipation and diarrhea.

Uva ursi would be my herb of choice if a long-standing problem indicated that kidney/bladder damage has occurred. Uva Ursi should be included in a formula for the prevention of passing of kidney stones as it will protect the kidneys from further damage and begin the repair of damage that has already occurred.

Uva ursi was prescribed for many years in European hospitals to postpartum (after the birth) women to reduce the risk of hemorrhage and aid the toning of the uterus to normal elasticity and size.

Anthilitic and Lithotriptic Herbs
(A Sub-category of Diuretic Herbs)

Anthilitic and lithotriptic herbs herbs work to prevent the formation of gravel and stones in the gall bladder and kidneys. They also help to dissolve and remove stones that have already formed. Some herbs used for this purpose are: **buchu leaves, butcher's broom, cascara sagrada, cornsilk, dandelion, devil's claw, gravel root, horsetail, hydrangea, marshmallow, parsley, stoneroot, uva ursi leaves,** and **white oak bark**.

Summary

Most of the diuretic, nephritic, anthilitic, and lithotriptic herbs are best combined in synergistic formulas, rather than used as individual herbs. Each formula should include herbs that are healing and demulcent along with the herbs specific to the urinary tract. Nephritic and the demulcent herbs lessen the likelihood of irritation and speed healing when added to a formula.

©**Copyright Butterfly Expressions, llc 2010   Butterfly Miracles with Herbal Remedies**

Chapter Eight
Diaphoretic and Sudorific Herbs

Diaphoretic herbs produce heat in the body. Sudorific herbs produce both heat and perspiration (sweating, and usually, lots of it). Bacteria and viruses are destroyed by heat and sweating aids the skin in eliminating the dead bacteria and other toxins from the body. A controlled fever is one of the best ways to kill critters and restore the body to health. Twenty-four to forty-eight hours of moderate fever (and sweating for at least part of that time) is usually sufficient in most instances.

It should be noted that if a person has a cold or other illness and does not run a fever, you can be quite sure that the immune system is weakened and is not responding properly to the attack that is being made upon the body. In this case, you would do well to react quickly with diaphoretic and sudorific herbs. I would recommend a mild stimulant as well, to get the body's defenses up and running.

The capillaries of the skin are so numerous that it is possible for them to hold nearly half the of blood contained by the whole body at one time, if the need arises. When the blood is pulled to the surface in this way by these herbal remedies and a sweat produced, the skin's very large surface area becomes a highly efficient eliminative organ. The increase of circulation throughout the body which occurs increases the healing effects of any herbal agents being used as the blood more efficiently carries nutrients to tissues and cells. Among the herbs listed as diaphoretics are powerful agents in fighting everything from colds through pneumonia. However, these herbs are so harmless and gentle that they can be used safely on infants and elderly, infirm individuals alike.

Blessed Thistle should be briefly mentioned here because it can be used effectively by nursing mother's without reducing their milk supply as a side effect of the fever and sweating.

Catnip is one of my favorites herbs, especially for infants and small children. This herb is especially useful for infants and children which have been prone to convulsions when feverish in the past. Catnip prevents or halts convulsions because it nourishes and soothes both nerves and muscles. Catnip halts convulsions almost instantaneously.

An indication for the choice of catnip from among the diaphoretic herbs would be a nervous disposition or pronounced nervousness or restlessness in this particular instance or illness. Catnip is especially noted for relieving the aches and pains that often accompany illness and fever.

Catnip is even more effective when mixed with chamomile in a glycerine base. This combination is excellent for colic and is safe for even the tiniest of infants. The glycerine makes it sweet enough that children who have experienced it once will often ask for it the next time.

Cayenne while not usually listed in this category, certainly acts in this capacity during illness. It is often the first and only herb I reach for. Cayenne is discussed in more detail on page 29.

Chamomile's action as a diaphoretic is not as dramatic as that of cayenne, ginger, or yarrow. Chamomile is often used with children and infants, with the elderly, or for persons who were debilitated by a chronic illness prior to the onset of this acute illness. Chamomile has a profound effect on a nervous stomach and on the nervous system in general, especially among children.   The calming effects of chamomile are, in part, due to the high content of calcium and magnesium found in this herb. It is important to note that chamomile flowers should never be boiled, as the volatile oils which contain much of the therapeutic value would be destroyed. Chamomile is particularly effective when tinctured in glycerine.

Ginger is similar in many ways to cayenne, but it is milder. These two wonderful herbs produce a great deal of heat in the body very rapidly. They should always be considered if the person is abnormally cold or weak. My favorite way to induce a good sweat is to place the sick person in a bathtub to which ginger has been added. I have used both the tincture and the powdered herb for this purpose. Ginger essential oil can be used but it is very strong. No more than 1 drop of ginger essential oil should be used at a time, even in the tub.   It is essential to wrap the person warmly upon leaving the tub, being very sure that they do not get chilled in any way. Leave them wrapped and sweating for at least 30 minutes. Most people, especially children, usually take a long nap after this treatment. When they wake, they find they have turned the corner on their illness. They may feel a little bit weak and shaky, but they are on the mend and will usually not get worse again later in the day.

Pleurisy Root, like chamomile, is less dramatic as a heat producer but has specific action for the lungs and the pleural sac surrounding them. It assists expectoration from the lungs and bronchial tubes, relieves inflammation, and has a tonic effect on the whole respiratory system. I rarely use this herb alone; rather I use it in combination with astringent and expectorant herbs. (Astringent herbs are discussed in chapter 11 and expectorant herbs are discussed in chapter 9. Actually, I use most herbs, with the notable exception of cayenne, in formulas that combine herbs from different categories. Herbs are much more effective used in this way.

Pleurisy root should not be used by itself when the skin is cold and the pulse is weak; a more stimulating diaphoretic would be more appropriate here. If the pleurisy root has been placed in a good combination, stimulant diaphoretics have already been added. Also, because of its strength and potency, its use for children should be cautious and always accompanied by a stimulant herb of some sort, such as peppermint or cayenne.

Yarrow when given hot and in quantity will raise the heat of the body, stimulate circulation and produce perspiration. Yarrow opens the pores and regulates the function of the liver while toning the mucous membranes of the stomach and bowels and aiding the glandular system. This in an impressive list of benefits for one herb to accomplish. Yarrow is excellent for stomach and intestinal upsets. It is a drying herb and should be used for head colds and bronchitis to clear catarrh from the lungs and the nasal passages.

Yarrow contains vitamins A, C, E, and F and some vitamin K. It also contains manganese, copper, potassium, iodine, and iron.

Blessed thistle, elderflowers, thyme, and **garden sage** are other excellent herbs in this category.

©**Copyright Butterfly Expressions, llc 2010   Butterfly Miracles with Herbal Remedies**

Chapter Nine
Febrifuge Herbs

Febrifuge is a more old-fashioned word for the modern medical term *antipyretic*. In general these two terms mean to reduce the temperature of the body when the temperature is abnormally high. Neither drugs nor herbs typically reduce body temperature if one does not have a fever. In other words, there is no danger of body temperatures falling too low when using either febrifuge/antipyretic herbs or drugs.

Non-herbal antipyretics, according to Wikipedia and a couple of medical sources, "cause the hypothalamus to override an interleukin-induced increase in temperature." What does this mean in simple English? The key to understanding that statement lies in understanding what is meant by the phrase "interleukin-induced increase in temperature."

Cytokines are proteins whose job within the body is to carry messages. It was once thought by science that the vast majority of communication within the body occurred along the nerves, and where there were no nerves, through the hormones somehow. It was known for a long time that there had to be another messenging system other than hormones because hormones are simply too slow to account for the speed with which messages travel in the body. Then cytokines were identified.

Interleukins are specialized cytokines that communicate between the different organs and cells of the **immune system.** They are the messengers that tell the immune when an invader organism is present, and then they give the various aspects of the immune system instructions as to what their specific role in countering this invasion should be. (There are specialized cytokines for other systems of the body as well as the immune system.)

Increased heat in the body is one way that the immune system fights off invasion by bacteria, viruses, etc. The need for additional heat, as well as leucocyte and T-cell response, is communicated by the **interleukin protein network**. Let's go back to the statement in paragraph two above and paraphrase it. *Non-herbal antipyretics (drugs), cause the <u>hypothalamus to override the interleukin's message to the immune system</u>*. This means that the increase in body temperature—fever—that the immune system sees a need for in order to kill the invading organisms is aborted. The body is prevented, by the drug, from running a fever as a method of killing the bacteria.

Is this reduction in temperature a good thing when the body is under attack by dangerous organisms? Does the absence of fever indicate wellness?* No,** but too many times it is assumed to be an indication of wellness and a child is returned to school when he is still contagious and still quite ill! The child feels better because antipyretic drugs, such as ibuprofen, acetaminophen, and aspirin are anti-inflammatories and pain relievers. ***The important thing to remember is that the child (or adult) is still sick, and probably, still contagious, although the drugs are masking the fever and making him think he is feeling better.

To do the medical world credit, it must be stated that when fever reduction medication is given by a doctor it is usually accompanied by an antibiotic in an attempt to kill the invaders even when the body temperature has been artificially reduced. If antibiotics had no side effects in the body, this scenario might be construed as a workable solution. When over-the-couter medicines are given at home by a concerned mother, no additional support is provided to the immune system in its fight against the

©Copyright Butterfly Expressions, llc 2010   Butterfly Miracles with Herbal Remedies

invading organisms and the immune system response has been altered by the fever-reducing drugs. Somehow, most of the time, the marvelous immune system manages to get the job done anyway! **So, what is the difference between antipyretic drugs and febrifuge herbs?** To answer that question properly I will need to explain—again, I'm sure—how herbal remedies work.

Herbal remedies work by bringing the body as quickly as possible into the best and most balanced state that can be achieved. In fever reduction, this means that if the immune system is out of kilter somehow and the fever being created to kill the invading organisms is getting too high, the herbs will act to lower the body temperature until it reaches safe levels. Too high a fever, as we have all been correctly taught, can cause organ and brain damage. Most, if not all, of the herbs in this category will also act to stimulate the immune system's other responses to the invasion while helping the body maintain a reasonable degree of fever. Herbs do not, in any way, over-ride the signals being sent by the immune system. Herbs act ALWAYS to strengthen and support the body's attempt to return to a normal, balanced and healthy state.

So, now, the really tricky question—**What is the difference between diaphoretic, sudorific, and febrifuge herbs?** HERBS ACT TO RETURN THE BODY TO A BALANCED AND HEALTHY STATE. If what you need is heat and antibiotic action, you will use herbs that are categorized as *diaphoretic*. If you need heat, antibiotic action, and a sweat to carry off the dead and dying critters, you will use herbs that are categorized as *sudorific*. If you need antibiotic action and the body temperature *reduced* slightly (remember, the immune system is out of balance, somehow, and not behaving properly), you would use a febrifuge herb. Febrifuge herbs lower the body temperature when it is dangerously high, fight the invasion of nasty organisms, and balance the immune system to work more effectively against them.

Is it complicated to decide which type of herb to use? NO, not at all. Let me illustrate why not by giving you a list of these types of herbs.

We will start with diaphoretic/sudorific herbs. Diaphoretics and sudorifics are listed together because they are the same list. The herb will decide, with the help of the immune system, whether or not a sweat is required. Producing a sweat is the only difference between a diaphoretic herb and a sudorific one.

Diaphoretic/Sudorific herbs: *bilberry, blessed thistle, brigham tea, catnip, chamomile, elder flowers,* **fenugreek,** *gentian, ginger, hyssop, pleurisy root,* sarsaparilla, *white willow, yarrow*

Febrifuge herbs: *bilberry, brigham tea, catnip, chamomile, elderflowers,* **fenugreek, garlic,** *gentian, ginger, hyssop, pleurisy root,* sarsaparilla, *white willow, yarrow.*

Only garlic is not classified as diaphoretic/sudorifics. Garlic is very unique in its effect on the body. Garlic does not produce heat, nor does it produce a sweat. Garlic has been considered for centuries to be the most perfect antibiotic that nature provides.

The herbs that are on both lists will act in the body exactly as the body needs them too. They may produce heat alone. They may produce heat with a sweat. If necessary they will lower the body temperature. In all three cases they will stimulate the immune system to greater and more effective action against the invading organisms. Amazing!!

Fenugreek and garlic will be discussed further in this chapter, along with a few more of the herbs that fit in all three categories. Sarsaparilla is discussed in chapter 13.

©**Copyright Butterfly Expressions, llc 2010   Butterfly Miracles with Herbal Remedies**

Bilberry is better known for several other healing actions than as a febrifuge, although it is outstanding in this category. Bilberries are used all over the world in the treatment of eye ailments such as cataracts, macular degeneration, and eye fatigue. During World War II, fighter pilots would consume bilberries to improve their night vision. Bilberries strengthen vein structure and are used effectively in the treatment of varicose veins and hemorrhoids. Perhaps it is the strengthening of the tiny blood vessels that feed the eyes that account, at least partially, for bilberry's effectiveness in eye health.

Bilberries are antiseptic and anti-inflammatory. They are used to treat inflammation in the nose and throat, and in the treatment of arthritis, gout, and digestive problems such as diarrhea.

Bilberries are an excellent source of antioxidants. They are high in chromium, which is an essential mineral for pancreatic health. The addition of bilberries to the diet, or taken as a supplement, often helps to stabilize blood sugar levels. Bilberries are closely related to blueberries, cranberries, and huckleberries. All of these fruits and berries share similar health benefits.

Brigham tea (Mormon tea) is an American relative of the Chinese herb, ma huang (also known as ephedra). However, it is so much milder that attempts to isolate its ephedrine compounds for drug production have proven cost prohibitive. For use as a tea, however, brigham tea has many of the same properties as ma huang—only much, much milder. I especially like it in the early stages of an illness where its diaphoretic/febrifuge activities are very helpful. I like it again later, during the recovery stages of the illness, because it offsets fatigue and strengthens the system. Brigham tea is a safe and effective diuretic, making it excellent during all stages of an illness.

Brigham tea, taken regularly, stimulates the immune system, and has often been effective in reducing allergy symptoms for the upcoming season. (If you wait to start drinking it until the allergies are upon you, it is probably too late to do much good for this season, although it is a mild decongestant.)

Fenugreek Besides being a febrifuge herb, fenugreek is used for women in estrogen related imbalances, especially during the menopause years. It has been effective, especially with other herbs such as blessed thistle, in increasing milk production in nursing women. Studies have found that fenugreek lowers cholesterol levels if taken over a long period of time. It is also associated with lowered risk of heart attacks. Fenugreek is recommended in the treatment of type 2 diabetes because of its specific action on the pancreas. Fenugreek also helps soothe gastrointestinal inflammation and is an effective remedy for heartburn and acid reflux. It is recommended that a little bit of fenugreek be taken before each meal for these ailments.

Fenugreek is a relatively strong herb, with some nervine properties. It should be used with caution for children, and probably, avoided altogether by pregnant women. In large quantity, or over a large period of time, it can occasionally cause nausea. Fenugreek has a lot of mucilaginous fiber. If you are taking any prescription medications, it is recommended that you take fenugreek either 2 hours before or 2 hours after taking the medications. The mucilaginous fiber may interfere with the absorption of the medications. These fibers make fenugreek tea a good remedy for skin inflammation.

Fenugreek seeds have been found to contain protein, vitamin C, niacin, potassium, and diosgenin (which is a compound that has properties similar to estrogen). Other active constituents in fenugreek are alkaloids, lysine and L-tryptophan, as well as steroidal saponins.

©Copyright Butterfly Expressions, llc 2010   **Butterfly Miracles with Herbal Remedies**

Garlic   Dr. Christopher, a renowned herbalist whose work is still greatly respected, lists garlic as an alterative, stimulant, diaphoretic, sudorific, diuretic, expectorant, antispasmodic, antiseptic, disinfectant, tonic, nervine, cathartic, emmenagogue, carminative, anthelmintic, rubefacient, vulnerary, antivenomous, condiment, anticatarrhal, digestant, antiparasitic, antibacterial, and antiviral. That is an impressive list for any herb! Dr. Christopher referred to garlic as "one of nature's masterpieces" and claimed it was "nature's own antibiotic."

Raw garlic, when crushed or chopped, releases a substance called allicin, which has been shown to be more powerfully antibiotic than penicillin and tetracycline. Garlic improves digestion, enhancing the absorption of other foods. It also strengthens the pancreas and increases the production of insulin, lowering blood sugar levels in diabetics.

Garlic acts as a powerful decongestant. With garlic's natural antibiotic properties, it is an excellent remedy for anything respiratory.   In addition, garlic helps to lower blood cholesterol and blood pressure. Garlic reduces the tendency of the blood to form clots inappropriately, thus preventing heart attack and strokes. Garlic dilates veins and arteries, increasing the flow of blood to the tissues and the removal of toxins from the cells. Garlic is a powerful antioxidant.

I use garlic predominantly in cooking and in a formula similar to Dr. Christopher's old standby, Anti-Plague. Although I rely on other herbs most of the time, I always know that if I meet a really nasty something, I have garlic to rely on and it will always be effective! I have seen garlic completely eradicate a staph infection that had gone on way too long.

White willow bark   The use of white willow bark has been documented way back in time in Europe, Asia, and Egypt. The Greek physician Hippocrates wrote about the medicinal properties of white willow in the 5th century B.C.

In 1829, some scientists in Europe published a report that the effective ingredient in white willow bark was a compound called salicin. Salicin is converted in the body to salicylic acid. Extracting the salicin from the bark proved to be expensive and timeconsuming, and it wasn't long before scientists created a synthetic form of salicylic acid. It became immediately apparent that the synthetic version was very hard on the stomach. At therapeutic doses, too many people developed stomach ulcers and bleeding.

A German company, Bayer (perhaps, you recognize the name), eventually developed a synthetic, less harsh derivative of salicylic acid and mass produced it under the name aspirin. Although claims were made that it was much less irritating, aspirin is still known, all these years later, for irritation to the stomach lining.

So, why use the synthetic form when God's own remedy is readily available? I don't have an answer for that question! Besides reducing fever, white willow bark is strongly anti-inflammatory. Research has shown that the salicin in white willow bark is not converted to salicylic acid until after it leaves the stomach, thus the salicylic acid does not irritate the stomach lining or anything else. Clinical trials have repeatedly shown that natural willow bark is more effective than aspirin because of other active compounds that are found in the bark but processed out of any drug made from the bark and not present at all in the synthetic versions.

White willow bark often has a long list of cautions in herbal references. Most of these cautions are based on what you would expect from aspirin (synthetic salicylic acid). I have used white willow bark for years and have never seen (or heard of from other herbal people) any negative effects whatsoever.

©Copyright Butterfly Expressions, llc 2010   Butterfly Miracles with Herbal Remedies

Chapter Ten
Expectorant and Demulcent Herbs

Expectorant herbs promote the liquefying and expulsion of mucus from the body. Expectorants fit into two general categories. There are the expectorants that facilitate expulsion of mucous from the trachea, lungs, or bronchi, and the ones that facilitate expulsion of mucous from the stomach or intestines.

Demulcent herbs are those which soothe and heal inflamed tissues.   I will discuss demulcent herbs here, in the same chapter as the expectorants, because so many of the good herbs cause the expelling of mucous and then heal and soothe as the next step and at the same time.

The following is a short list of my favorites in this category.   I will not try to tell you here <u>all</u> of the healing uses of any one of them. ***These herbs are the great healers of the plant kingdom. Each one merits an intense study of its other medicinal properties!***

Comfrey   To do comfrey justice would take pages and pages. It has been one of the most important first aid remedies known to men for centuries. It's use in the healing of wounds and broken bones is, perhaps, its most important and well-known function. I will quote a great herbalist, Dr. Shook, who said, "It does not seem to matter much which part of the body is broken or torn, either externally or internally, comfrey will heal it quickly. It is a great cell proliferant (stimulator of new cell growth); it grows new flesh and bone alike, stops hemorrhage, and is wonderful for coughs, soothing and healing the inflamed tissues in a most remarkable manner." It is in the soothing of coughs and inflamed tissues that the demulcent properties are seen.

Mullein   In reviewing my herbal notes to write this segment I found such references as "mullein has a particular affinity for the respiratory organs" and "mullein is of particular use in pulmonary complaints" and "mullein is particularly useful to the urinary tract and the eliminative organs" and "mullein is particularly useful in calming and quieting inflamed and irritated nerves". In other words, mullein is useful in just about any circumstance and with any body system.

Mullein has the unique distinction of being both astringent (drying to tissues) when drying is needed and demulcent (healing and soothing) when this is needed. I personally add mullein to a great many formulas, especially kidney/bladder ones, as a protective agent and to guarantee that accidental overuse will not result in further irritation and possible damage. You never make a mistake with the choice of mullein.

Marshmallow, discussed in the previous chapter, is a very nice demulcent herb. The mallows are readily available in the mountain west area. There are many species of marshmallow. None of them are toxic in the least and all are healing in similar ways to one another. It would be hard to find an herb that has as many listed uses or is found in as many herbal formulas as is marshmallow.

Slippery Elm is in a class by itself because of its ability to neutralize stomach acids and aid digestion. Slippery Elm is particularly useful in the digestion of the proteins found in dairy products. Slippery Elm soothes mucous membranes throughout the body. By this I mean that this amazing herb will soothe irritation and inflammation in the stomach, intestinal tract, urinary tract, gall bladder, reproductive organs, and the respiratory system. Slippery Elm removes mucus faster and more gently than any other herbs that I have ever used. Slippery Elm is very nutritious—much like oatmeal—but is very easy on the stomach. It is an excellent herb for the convalescent stage of illness.

Elecampane is often used in cough and respiratory formulas, but is rarely used alone. Elecampane is a great expectorant and has some unique antiseptic properties. Elecampane is often the expectorant of choice because it nourishes and balances the pancreas and is one of the richest sources of natural insulin. Elecampane could also be classed as a diaphoretic and diuretic herb. The potassium chloride in elecampane gently cleanses the liver and the calcium chloride content strengthens the heart muscle.

Licorice root is different from other herbs in this category because the list of vitamins and minerals that it contains are very different from these herbs. Licorice should definitely be classed as an expectorant and a demulcent because of its great healing properties, but it works from a different point of view. Licorice contains glycosides (rather than potassium chloride and calcium chloride) as the expectorant agent. Licorice is also a source of the female hormone estrogen.

Licorice is a very stimulating herb, which makes it an excellent choice when recovering from a debilitating or lengthy illness. Licorice root is ***contra-indicated for people with certain types of heart conditions***. Don't let the previous statement frighten you. The result of use with these people will be a rapid pulse (possibly erratic) which will subside very shortly. These symptoms should be used, however, as a signal to chose a different herb from this category for use next time.

An interesting note about expectorant herbs is that they **all** (except Licorice as noted above) contain potassium chloride. This seems to be the key to their expectorant properties as potassium chloride causes the mucous to become liquefied and soluble while restoring the proper balance of electrolytes and salts to the blood.

These herbs, while frequently taken internally with great effect, can also be applied as poultices. The combination of warmth and moisture that characterizes a poultice adds to their effectiveness.

Other expectorant herbs **black cohosh, coltsfoot, flaxseed, ginger, ginseng, horehound, hops, ipecacuanha, myrrh, onion, pleurisy root, red root, saw palmetto, shepherd's purse, spikenard, St. John's wort, vervain, and wild sage.** Most of the herbs in this list are demulcent to some estent.

Other demulcent herbs include **blue cohosh, cayenne, coltsfoot, corn silk, fenugreek, flaxseed, goldenseal, hops, lobelia, marshmallow, plantain, rice, sarsaparilla, sesame, and slippery elm bark**

©**Copyright Butterfly Expressions, llc 2010   Butterfly Miracles with Herbal Remedies**

Chapter Eleven
Nervine, Antispasmodic, and Analgesic Herbs

The purpose of a nervine herb is not to relieve pain, although that is often the result. Pain should be viewed as a friend because it is the body's way of alerting us to the fact that something is wrong and needs our attention. While you might often use a nervine or antispasmodic herb to relieve acute pain, the remedy should _always_ be followed by an attempt to find and eliminate the underlying cause of the pain. For example, you might successfully use BBL tincture to deaden the pain of a toothache or a headache, but unless you address the cavity in the tooth or the lack of sleep that created the headache, the BBL is only a band-aid. Sooner or later the pain will increase. Worse, however, will be that nothing has been done to address the cause.

The myelin sheaths of the nerves are one of the first things to suffer in a nutritional deficiency, especially if the situation includes a lack of B vitamins. The undernourished or damaged nerves are the cause of the pain. It is a very great blessing that the herbs that deaden pain also contain the missing nutrients to heal and rebuild nerves. Isn't nature wonderful? People take the remedy as though it were a pain reliever, but in reality, they are nourishing and strengthening the nerves all the while!

Let's define these two classes of herbs—nervines and antispasmodics. Nervines are herbal agents that feed, regulate, strengthen, and rebuild the nerve cells of the body. Nervines fall into two categories, sedatives and nerve stimulants. Sedative herbs relax the nerves and dull pain. Nerve stimulants improve mental and emotional stamina. Both types of nervines heal and nourish.

Antispasmodics are herbs which prevent or relieve excessive spasms of both voluntary and involuntary muscles. These are treated together in most herbal texts because the distinction is often hard to draw. Many antispasmodics work because of their action on the nerves and most nervines are also antispasmodic.

The beauty of herbal nervines and antispasmodics is that they are **NOT** narcotic in any way. They do not cause addiction and they heal without harmful side effects. The body metabolizes them like any other food, leaving no ill effects or residues behind. _**It is a complete mystery to me why pain killers are so popular when the herbal world contains agents that are just as strong and effective but lacking in side effects and harmless to the liver!**_

I have chosen to give only a few sentences about each one. My focus is to highlight the differences in usage between one herb and another, and to list any safety data that might be helpful. In actuality (real life) I rarely use any nervine herb by itself. They are much more effective and manageable in formulas, each formula tweaked just a little to be particularly effective in certain circumstances or for certain people.

For a complete treatise on each herb you will need to consult an herbal guidebook or just go online and type in the name of the herb you are interested in learning more about.

Lobelia Chapter 5 contains a short treatise on the uses of lobelia, by far the greatest of the herbs in this category, especially when used in conjunction with the cohoshes and blue vervain.

Skullcap Another great herb in this category is skullcap, which is used predominately for insomnia, hysteria, nervous headache, convulsions, and any ailment that is accompanied by both restlessness and fever. Skullcap is slower acting but more permanent in its action. It has no side effects and may—in fact, should—be taken regularly for quite a period of time for maximum effect. Combined with cayenne and goldenseal, skullcap is said to strengthen the heart muscle.

©Copyright Butterfly Expressions, llc 2010   Butterfly Miracles with Herbal Remedies

Valerian is a very interesting herb. Valerian looks quite similar to many other members of the umbelliferae family, but it is easily identified by the obnoxious odor of it's roots and stems. The best way I can think to describe it is as a mixture of a smelly sock and a dead mouse!! Most people find Valerian gently stimulating and very soothing to the nervous system. A very few people react very strongly to Valerian; it will be extremely stimulating or very sedating. This caution is discussed in more detail on page 32 in the chapter on stimulant herbs. Unless you are one of the rare people who over-react to valerian, this herb should be a vital part of any herbal nervine program.

Valerian has a few very unique characteristics. One of these is that valerian *influences the circulation by slowing the action of the heart while increasing its force.* This makes it a leading component of remedies dealing with erratic heart beats, palpitations, and heart muscle weakness. It is also very useful for children during illnesses when their little hearts are racing and the pulse is abnormally rapid. Remember to use appropriately small quantities with children.

Valerian has a sedative effect upon the nervous system and can be used as a tranquilizer or sleep aid. Instead of leaving one feeling groggy or sluggish it produces a feeling of refreshment and vitality. For this reason it is usually categorized as a stimulant herb. Valerian is usually recommended for short-term use and caution is advised with children. I would definitely agree with these recommendations if valerian were being used by itself. Combined with the cohoshes, blue vervain, lobelia, and other nervines, it is a standard at my house, especially for children!! (See BBL on page 113) Valerian and a close relative, spikenard, are frequently used in essential oil form. As an essential oil both of these herbs are amazing and highly recommended!

Mistletoe is an herb that is used predominantly to stop excessive menstrual bleeding, bleeding after childbirth, or bleeding associated with ovarian cysts. Misteltoe is used to strengthen vein, artery, and capillary walls. Consider this herb for repair of damage after a stroke or a blood clot. I find valerian's mild sedative properties an added advantage at these times. In my opinion mistletoe should be used for a short time for a specific condition, rather than long-term. I have never seen anything in the literature to indicate that long-term use is a problem, but I have found that it lowers blood pressure too dramatically in some people when used for long periods of time.

Lady slipper is a leading herb is this category but has become almost extinct. It is extremely expensive and getting more and more difficult to purchase. Constituent wise, the combining of the herbs motherwort and passion flower makes an excellent substitute for this wonderful herb in nervine formulas. I save lady slipper for use with a particular type of miscarriage situation; it has worked miracles in that regard several times.

Cramp bark, hops, motherwort, passion flower, peppermint, squawvine, St. John's wort, eucalyptus, spearmint, and **black cohosh** are a few of the other valuable herbs in this category.

Many nervine herbs are relaxing in small doses, especially when taken warm; over done these herbs can be highly stimulating, even irritating.

Analgesic herbs are those that are used to relieve pain. Most of these herbs are the nervines and antispasmodics listed and discussed in this chapter. Depending on the situation, pain relief herbs can be used either internally or externally (as a pack or liniment. It is often best to use them both ways simultaneously. (See PPAC formula in the recipes section of this booklet.)

©Copyright Butterfly Expressions, llc 2010   Butterfly Miracles with Herbal Remedies

Chapter Twelve
The Astringent Herbs

Let's begin by defining the word astringent as it applies to herbs.   Astringent herbs contract the tissues, and thereby, arrest or limit discharges. These discharges may be from any organ or system. Some examples would be the intestinal area in diarrhea, hemorrhages from uterus, lungs, etc., and accumulations of mucous in the glands and tissues. This contracting and drying of the tissues is generally accomplished because of the tannic acid content of the herb. The tannic acid content varies greatly from herb to herb. This means there is a lot variation in the strength of different herbs and the reaction produced in the body.

There are hundreds of herbs out there with astringent properties. Many of them work on more than one system of the body. I will mention a few notable ones here—my favorites, of course.

Bayberry is one of the most impressive of the astringents. It is of particular note for diarrhea. Bayberry is the base herb in the recipe for what was known in the early 1900's as composition powder. This amazing formula (called COMP at Butterfly Express, llc) is the first response for colds, sore throats, and anything viral—particularly in the head and upper respiratory areas. Bayberry bark promotes proper glandular activity throughout the body. White oak is similar in some respects to bayberry, but lacks certain stimulant characteristics.

Black Walnut leaves (and hulls) This astringent herb is also antiviral and anti fungal. My favorite use of black walnut is to fight ringworm and other skin infestations and sores. I usually use the hulls for this purpose as they are slightly stronger. Green hulls work well and do not leave dark purple/black staining on skin or clothing.   Black walnut can also be used as a douche to fight vaginal yeast. Black walnut is anthelminthic (rids the body of worms) but it strips the intestinal tract. There are other, better ways to accomplish this. Black walnut balances the glandular system with a particular affinity for the thyroid.

Red Raspberry is frequently used by women of child-bearing age during pregnancy. Red raspberry is a mild astringent which gently contracts and tones the entire reproductive system. The hormones of pregnancy loosen muscle structures so that the uterus and surrounding muscles, can stretch to accommodate the growing fetus.   This loosening often results in the interesting symptoms of pregnancy such as constipation (or occasionally, diarrhea), frequent urination, bleeding gums, and pain in joints and tendons. Red Raspberry, taken as a tea or tincture, greatly reduces these symptoms while still allowing the uterus to expand and the hips to move apart as needed. How can it do both things at the same time? Herbs bring the body into a state of balance. Constipation is not normal but a softening uterus during pregnancy is.

Red Raspberry is often overlooked (I have certainly been guilty here) by herbalists when not dealing with the symptoms of pregnancy. Fortunately for me, my own midwife insisted that at least two cups of it be consumed every day. Red raspberry could be used with good benefit in most cases of diarrhea, constipation, stomach and intestinal upset, and hemorrhoids. It should be considered by diabetics to stabilize the pancreas. Red raspberry is frequently used for sore mouth, sore throat, and spongy gums. It is a main ingredient in formulas that are used in the eyes.

A wild form of raspberry, called thimbleberry, is very effective and grows abundantly in the mountain west. I love to harvest this one because the leaves are huge and you can harvest so much in so little time!

©**Copyright Butterfly Expressions, llc 2010   Butterfly Miracles with Herbal Remedies**

Shepherd's Purse is one of the best astringent plants known to man. It is excellent for water retention due to kidney problems. The place where shepherd's purse really shines is in any type of internal bleeding, even those of hemorrhage proportions. I have used shepherd's purse with great success many times to stop a postpartum (after childbirth) hemorrhage, and to slow or stop heavy menstrual bleeding. Shepherd's purse can also be used for bloody urine, bleeding from the lungs, bleeding stomach ulcers, and nosebleeds—any bleeding which begins internally. A very, very excellent herb.

White Oak is one of the most valuable astringent herbs because it is useful for both external and internal bleeding. It heals damaged and inflamed tissues of the skin, mucous membranes, stomach and intestines. *A tea of the bark makes an excellent wash for gum infection, a gargle for sore throats, and a corrective for diarrhea.*

White Oak is one of the few herbs I have even seen listed (and had any success with) as an *antidote for drug reactions and chemotherapy side effects.*

Witch Hazel is a valuable and soothing astringent. It is especially useful for the lungs, stomach, nose, rectum, uterus, and kidneys. Applied externally it has a great influence on the veins and capillaries, making it excellent for varicose veins, bruises, insect bites, wounds and external bleeding.

Yarrow is an herb that should be listed here and in several other sections. Yarrow helps to regulate the function of the liver and glandular system and tones the membranes of the stomach and bowels. It acts as a blood cleanser and opens the pores for the elimination of toxins and wastes, bringing great relief to the kidneys. It's astringent action can be used to trigger the dumping of gallstones and kidney stones. The fresh plant placed on an open wound will cause almost instant coagulation of the blood and the sealing of the tissues together. Yarrow is discussed in more detail on page 32.

Yellow Dock has been a very popular herb for constipation, skin diseases, blood diseases, arthritis, and indigestion for many years. I have used it and appreciated it many times myself. Yellow dock, however, is an alterative herb with a pronounced ability to cleanse the liver. This can be a good thing! Dr. John R. Christopher loved this herb and used it well. But the world was a very different place in his day. Comparatively, people took far less over-the-counter and prescription medications, there were less pollutants in the air, less use of chemical fertilizers, and less dyes and additives in our foods. When he used yellow dock to "dump" a liver, he had little danger of the reaction being more than he bargained for. I like herbal cleansing to be gentle and at a controlled pace. I use 1/4 to 1/2 the recommended amount of yellow dock in any recipe that I find if I suspect the recipe is from a former time when the food supply was cleaner and less deadly. I like it added to formulas in the lesser amounts because keeping the liver clean and healthy prevents such a long list of ailments. *This is a great herb but must be used with caution in our day. Use this marvellous herb, just use it with good sense.*

Other astringent herbs include: agrimony, bilberries, black cohosh, buchu, calendula, cinnamon bark, cloves, comfrey root, cramp bark, echinacea, elecampane, garden sage, goldenrod, gravel root, hawthorne, hops, horsetail, juniper berries, myrrh, pipsissiwa, red raspberry, squawvine, uva ursi, and wood betony.

Styptic herbs A subcategory of astringents, styptic herbs are applied externally to constrict the capillaries and blood vessels to arrest local bleeding —you cut yourself shaving—or hemorrhaging—your cut your finger badly. Some styptic herbs are bayberry, comfrey, cayenne, plantain, stinging nettle, witch hazel and my personal favorite, yarrow. Yarrow, in herb or essential oil form, is the first thing that I would use for topical applications.

©Copyright Butterfly Expressions, llc 2010   Butterfly Miracles with Herbal Remedies

Chapter Thirteen
Alterative and Adaptogenic Herbs

Alteratives are herbal agents that gradually alter and improve the body chemistry through purification of the blood. Alteratives accomplish gradual changes in metabolism and tissue function and can be used effectively in both acute and chronic conditions. *Adaptogenic* herbs are a subcategory of alteratives in that they are the herbs in the alterataive category that improve and regulate immune function.

I find that the categories get a little muddy when talking about tonic, alterative, and adaptogenic herbs. Let me try to clarify the terminology a little bit. Tonic herbs (chapter 5) gradually improve the tone and function of a system or organ of the body. That definition makes the herbs listed here *tonic* herbs. The difference between the herbs on the tonic list and the herbs listed here is the phrase, used above, ***improves the body chemistry through the purification of the blood.*** Alterative herbs are blood cleansers and adaptogenic herbs are blood cleansers that specifically improve the immune system. It is difficult to list the adaptogenic herbs separately because nearly all immune system improving herbs have marked effects on other systems of the body also.

Some alterative and adaptogenic herbs are: aloe vera, alfalfa, burdock, brigham tea, black cohosh, blue cohosh, cleavers, chapparal, dandelion, echinacea, elder flower, garlic, ginseng, goldenseal, nettles, oregon grape, plantain, poke root, red clover, sarsaparilla, sassafras, yarrow, and yellow dock.

Chaparral is a somewhat controversial herb. In your search for natural cancer remedies, you will certainly come across chaparral. It was, and still is, used by native Americans in the treatment of cancer. There are a great many anecdotal stories about cancers, both internal and external, that were cured by chaparral. There are even some clinical trials that seem to support chaparral as a cancer cure. These trials attribute chaparral's cancer fighting properties to the presence of an ingredient called nor-kihihydroguairetic (NDGA) and a powerful antioxidant enzyme SOD, of which chapparal has more than any other plant known.

Being a blood purifier, chaparral has been used for a multitude of ailments, with good report. Chaparral is said to have analgesic, expectorant, antibacterial, antviral, and strong anti-inflammatory properties. I know from personal experience that it is a very strong astringent and very effective at drying up mucous in the lungs and intestines. I rarely use it, however, and never for more than a few days because it is so drying to mucous membranes such as inside the nose and the vaginal area. If I were in a fight with cancer, however, I would tolerate the side effects cheerfully and make full use of chaparral's very strong medicinal properties. Just a word of warning—chaparral tastes absolutely horrible.

Chaparral, as a mouthwash, is listed in nearly every herbal reference. It would take a great deal of courage to use this nasty tasting herb as a mouthwash. The tea is also used in the treatment of skin diseases, bruises, herpes and eczema.

It has been claimed that chaparral causes everything from hepatitis to kidney and colon cancer, but no reliable evidence for any such claims exist, as far as I can determine. Chaparral is a ***very*** strong herb, however, and common sense and reasonable caution should be exercised. Extreme caution should be used with children and chaparral should never be used with infants. In my opinion, there is almost always a better herb than chaparral, except in a fight with cancer. If you do feel the need to use it, limit the length of time that you take it, or alternate it with other alterative herbs and add some demulcent herbs to your regimen. I would be very hesitant to recommend chaparral to anyone else as a remedy.

©**Copyright Butterfly Expressions, llc 2010   Butterfly Miracles with Herbal Remedies**

Dandelion increases the flow of bile which improves digestion and greatly enhances the absorption of vitamins and minerals. In addition, dandelion itself, contains many nutrients, including iron, a whole list of easily assimilable minerals, a wide spectrum of B vitamins, and a huge amount of vitamin A. Many herbalists consider dandelion root a specific for hypoglycemia and diabetes. Typically, the young leaves are consumed in the spring if they are available and the root is used during the rest of the year. Be sure to harvest your dandelion where commercial weed sprays have not been.

Echinacea is one of the very best adaptogenic herbs. Some information on it has been provided on page 30. To really do this herb credit would take many pages. I highly recommend that you study this one in detail, both in this booklet and from other sources.

Elder Flower is considered one of the greatest and most versatile herbs because of its ability to cleanse the cells of the body from toxic waste. Among its many constituents are agents that act as sedatives, pain relievers, expectorants, anti-inflammatories, as well as ones that reduce fevers and increase circulation. Elder flower and peppermint combine well to deal with fever, flu, and cold symptoms. Alternatively, elder flower is combined with catnip for fever, flu, and cold symptoms, especially for infants. For infections, combine elder flower with yarrow and oregon grape. For lung and bronchial congestion, mullein should be added.

Garlic Garlic, one of the very best adaptogenic herbs, is discussed on page 52.

Ginseng. Ginseng, worldwide, is probably the most used and most widely studied herb of all. The information can be confusing, and a little misleading, until you have sufficient knowledge to sort the various species of ginseng. Panax ginseng, also known as Korean or Chinese ginseng, is the most widely used and extensively studied. Panax ginseng is considered to be the strongest medicinally. Four closely related species are also used medicinally. These are Panax quinquefolium (American ginseng), Panax Japonicum, (Japanese ginseng) Panax pseudoginseng (Himalayan ginseng) and Panax trifolium. Of these quinquefolium (or American ginseng) seems to be the closest in chemical composition to the more expensive and more difficult to obtain Panax ginseng (Korean or Chinese ginseng). Another variety, Siberian ginseng, (which is not a true ginseng at all) will be discussed at the end of this ginseng section.

Ginseng is processed in two forms: white and red. White is the dried root with the outer skin peeled off. Red is whole root which has been steamed. Obviously, steaming or removing the outer layer both alter the final chemical composition of the end products. I do not know why the outer layer is removed or why the ginseng is steamed. It would seem to me that leaving it alone would be best; I trust there is a reason.

There are many types and grades of ginseng depending on the source, age, and parts used, and on the methods of preparation. Old, wild roots are considered the most potent and the main or tap root is reputed to have the highest medicinal value. For economic reasons, much of the ginseng on the market is of poor quality and often blended with adulterants. Good quality roots and products are available, however, with a little effort and persistence.

In Chinese Medical literature and lore, ginseng is said to restore yang qualities and is often used in male tonics and medicines and to restore female functions that are the result of too much yin. Translated (roughly) to western thought, this means to balance the male and female hormones. Ginseng is very effective in women whose estrogen levels are too high, putting them at risk for certain cancers and more likely to suffer ill effects at menopause. Emotionally, following eastern medical philosophy, ginseng balances the passive/aggressive, nurturing/providing (Fire and Water) aspects of our personalities.

©Copyright Butterfly Expressions, llc 2010   Butterfly Miracles with Herbal Remedies

The list of uses for any variety of ginseng is very long in every book on herbal medicine that I have ever seen. I will discuss a few of the most interesting and lesser known facts about ginseng on this page.

The most noted effects of ginseng are in the slowing of the onset of both mental and physical fatigue when the body or mind is under great stress. These effects have been demonstrated in both animal studies and double-blind, clinical trials in humans. In studies conducted in the early 1960's the time to physical fatigue during endurance tests was shown to be lengthened by the ingestion of ginseng. Mental acuity and the ability to work longer with less mistakes was documented among radio operators. The analogy that comes to mind is that stimulant herbs are like stepping on the gas while ginseng is more like giving the engine a tune-up.

Other noted, and well-studied, uses for ginseng are: in the treatment of diabetes, as a reproductive system tonic and healer, for its immunostimulant properties, in the strengthening of liver function, protecting and strengthening the cardiovascular system, in the protection of cells during radiation, and the rebuilding of damaged cells when the radiation treatment is finished. Ginseng has been shown in clinical trials to have anti-cancer properties.

A species of plant, **Eleutherococcus senticosus**, often referred to as **siberian ginseng** is a much used substitute for the Panax varieties discussed above. Not being of the Panax genus at all, siberian ginseng has a very different chemical composition; it contains no ginsenosides at all. However, it is a great alterative and adaptogenic herb in its own right. In most respects it is just as effective as the more expensive, and harder to obtain in good quality, Panax varieties. Siberian ginseng has been shown to produce similar effects on mental and physical stamina. It is as effective in the reduction of sugar levels and lipids in the bloodstream, in toning the adrenal glands, and in regulating blood pressure as Panax ginseng and the other closely related varieties.

I find it very interesting that reliable clinical trials have shown conclusively that two such different plants could have such similar effects on the human body. It is a wonderful illustration of the fact that there is more than one way to accomplish cures in the body. This leads me, once more, to the conclusion postulated in the early chapter of this book. One of the reasons, perhaps the biggest reason, herbs work is because they provide the body with badly needed basic nutrition. How much "chemical constituency" and "active ingredients" account for herbal cures, and how much should be attributed to basic nutrition?

One notable difference in these two herbs: *Panax varieties have repeatedly been shown to be most effective when the body and mind are already showing adverse signs of reaction to stress. Eleuthero, (Siberian Ginseng) on the other hand, when given to healthy humans subjects in clinical trials who were then subjected to adverse physical and mental conditions, were shown to increase the ability to withstand the <u>additional</u> stress*.

After giving this information considerable thought, I began using the two varieties together—acting on the assumption that most of us have some body systems that are already showing signs of debilitation from stress, while other systems are still in good working order for the moment. This has been borne out by muscle testing. How I ask the question, and which body system I am asking about, affects the form of ginseng that is most appropriate to use. Often—more times than not—both are requested in most instances. Some very interesting things to think about here.

©**Copyright Butterfly Expressions, llc 2010   Butterfly Miracles with Herbal Remedies**

Goldenseal and Oregon grape Goldenseal is, of course, a very renowned herb. It is considered a Chinese herb but is used widely all over the world. Michael T. Murray, N.D. has conducted vigorous laboratory trials of the constituents of herbs. He claims that oregon grape has nearly the same constituents as goldenseal. Goldenseal is sometimes contra indicated for people with pancreatic problems (diabetics and those suffering from hypo or hyperglycemia). Oregon grape is missing the molecular compound that is responsible for this contra indication.

I have found, during the years that I have used herbs, that a plant that grows in one's own area (as opposed to one grown in, say, China) is usually more effective for people living in that region. For that reason, and because oregon grape is much cheaper or can be wild crafted, I tend to use it in most of my formulas. I have been doing this for years and I have gotten the same excellent results that I used to obtain when using goldenseal in those same formulas.

Oregon grape and goldenseal both exhibit a broad spectrum of antibiotic activity because of their berberine content. These plants are effective against bacteria, protozoa and fungi, including staphylococcus and streptomyces species. The action of these herbs is actually stronger than many of the pharmaceutical antibiotics, but does not allow the overgrowth of candida albicans that so often accompanies prescription antibiotic use. In addition, berberine increases the blood supply to the spleen, greatly enhancing immune system function.

Plants containing berberine also have excellent diuretic and diaphoretic properties. Either one of these herbs, by itself or in a formula, is an excellent response to most types of acute illnesses.

Plantain is a great healer and is used both internally and externally. Used as a poultice or a soak, plantain will remove the infections and then heal the wound in even very advanced cases of infection in wounds, particularly in the extremities of the body. Plantain with mullein and poke root is unsurpassed as a remedy for infected wounds!

Enzymes found in plantain are used for stomachache, diarrhea, mild intestinal inflammation, hemorrhoids, and bladder inflammations. The fresh juice contains the most enzymes, of course. Fresh juice of plantain is almost miraculous in the healing of stomach ulcers. Even as a tincture, plantain is useful for all of these conditions. Plantain seeds are very similar to psyllium seeds; they are both member of the plantago species. Plantain seeds can be used similarly to psyllium seeds in the treatment of bowel problems.

Both plantain leaf and root are useful in treating chronic lung conditions, especially in children. A mild tea of plantain makes an excellent eye wash for infection in the eyes.

Plantain often grows in close proximity to water where mosquitoes are likely to breed and it is excellent for the treatment of mosquito bites. Simply macerate (mash and cut) the leaves a little and rub on or apply to the bites. This can be easily accomplished by simply chewing the leaves for a moment. The enzymes you will get this way will also be good for you! Plantain, used this way, will also stop bleeding from minor cuts and wounds.

Poke Root is one of the strongest of the alterative category of herbs. ***It should by taken internally in very moderate doses.*** Larger doses can become strongly emetic (cause vomiting). Poke root is best used in conjunction with other alterative and antibacterial/antviral herbs. Formulas such as these are excellent for chronic respiratory ailments. Poke root is astringent and helps to dry up mucous and

©**Copyright Butterfly Expressions, llc 2010   Butterfly Miracles with Herbal Remedies**

catarrh. These formulas are used for kidney infections and for draining enlarged lymphatics. In fact, poke root is the best herb I know for encouraging lymphatic circulation and drainage. Poke root has a strong and specific action on the entire glandular system, but has a particular affinity for the thyroid and the spleen.

Poke root is excellent added to a poultice for drawing infections out of the body, even when there is no open wound (such as in cases of breast infection, lung infection, inflamed bowel, etc.). Poke root is a major ingredient in packs for breast infections in nursing mothers.

Red Clover is considered a mild adaptogenic and blood cleansing herb. As such, red clover has action on the entire system through the gentle and gradual purifying of the blood. Red clover specifically enhances and strengthens the immune system. This herb is generally an ingredient in anti-infectious formulas, rather than being used by itself as an infection fighter. Used in combination with yarrow and elder flower, red clover is very potent. In recent studies, red clover is showing promise as a treatment for cancer.

Interestingly, used by itself or with herbs such as comfrey, red clover aids in the rebuilding of the cartilage in damaged knees or backs where the discs have been compressed.

Sarsaparilla   Laboratory evidence strongly indicates that sarsaparilla is an endotoxin binder. Endotoxins are bacteria that are absorbed back into the bloodstream from a congested intestinal tract. A normally functioning liver filters endotoxins and other toxins from the blood. If the liver is unable to perform this function properly a host of nasty symptoms follow.

Endotoxins circulating in the blood are responsible for much of the inflammation and cell damage that occurs in such diseases as gout and arthritis. They are often the underlying cause of skin problems such as psoriasis and excema. These types of skin conditions will not clear up without an internal cleanse and the elimination of the bacteria from the bloodstream. Endotoxins bind to certain nutrients found in sarsaparilla. Bound in this way they pass harmlessly from the body through the urinary system. Sarsaparilla is often added, usually in only a small quantity, to many anti-inflammatory and anti-infectious formulas.

It should be noted that a clogged colon can allow any toxic substance, including cancer cells, to circulate freely throughout the body by using the bloodstream to travel.

Yellow Dock is discussed on page 58.

Conclusion

Herbs in the alterative/adaptogenic category accomplish the best of what alternative therapies are supposed to be about. First and foremost, herbs should be about prevention and the strengthening of the entire system. Alternative therapy is not so much about how to cope with the flu as it is about how to become so "bullet-proof" that you don't even catch the flu when it comes around.

Alterative and adaptogenic herbs, used on a regular basis, will bring you increased resistance to disease and stress, and more stamina and vitality every day of your life!

©Copyright Butterfly Expressions, llc 2010   Butterfly Miracles with Herbal Remedies

Body Systems Affected
by
Colon Congestion

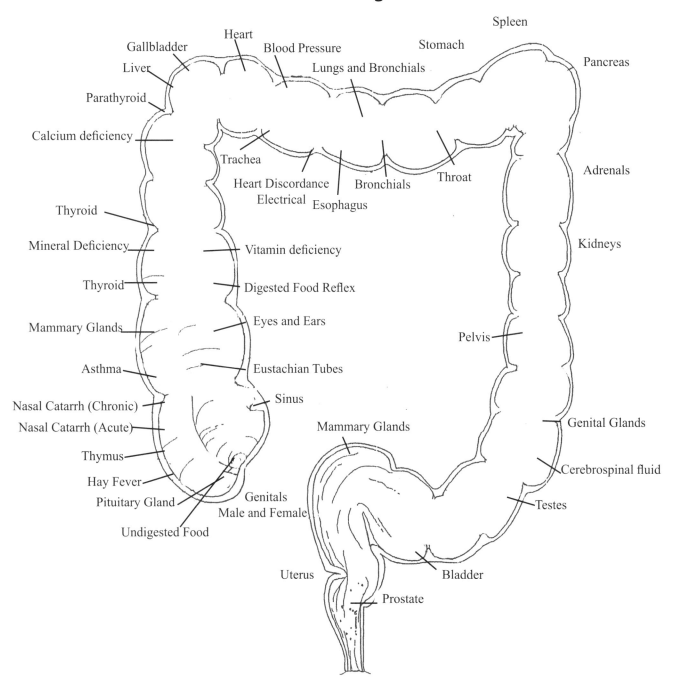

There are trace minerals that are absolutely essential to health. These minerals (elements) are absorbed and made available to the body from different sections of the colon. When the walls of the colon are encrusted with old fecal matter or inflammation is present due to food allergies, these minerals are not available to the body. Fortunately, each mineral is absorbed from more than one section of the colon. This is only of benefit as long as there are parts of the colon still in pretty good health. Keeping the colon in good working order is one of the best things that you can do for your health.

Chapter Fourteen
Emmenagogue and Hormone Balancing Herbs

The definition of an emmenagogue herb is that the herb promotes the **normal** flow of blood to the pelvic area. There are nearly 200 herbs listed in this category, as nearly as I can tell.

The focus of some of these herbs is to start menstrual cycles when they are missing. Other herbs are taken to increase the efficiency with which the endometrial lining of the uterus pulls away at the time of menstruation. Still other herbs are taken to staunch the excess bleeding that some women experience with their flow. Other herbs are taken to relieve the symptoms of PMS. Although most of these 200 herbs do promote blood flow to the pelvic area, their major focus is in these other directions. In addition, nearly all of these herbs have action in many other parts of the body. Herbs is this category are some of the great nourishing, strengthening, tonic, and adaptogenic herbs in nature's pharmacy.

Some female problems might be related to the flow of blood to the pelvic area. They could just as easily be the result of hormone imbalances, nutritional deficiencies, an acute illness, a chronic illness, an accident or emotional upset, or problems in the nerves. Any herb that clears any of these underlying conditions could be—and probably has been—listed as an emmenagogue.

In this chapter I will list some of the herbs that benefit the female reproductive system. I will include in the list some herbs that strengthen the nerves that are often damaged or upset by hormonal imbalances. I will discuss a few of my favorites from the list in more detail.

Since herbs bring body systems into balance, it is not critically important that you understand which herbs are estrogenic, It is important, however, to know which emmenagogue herbs promote contraction of the uterine muscles and stimulate bleeding. These herbs should always be avoided during pregnancy. There are a few other herbs that should be used sparingly, or not at all, during pregnancy. A list of the herbs to avoid or use with caution during pregnancy will be provided at the end of this chapter. Please pay close attention to this list if you are pregnant.

Some herbs that balance and strengthen the female reproductive system are: black cohosh, blue cohosh, buchu, chamomile, catnip, comfrey, cramp bark, dandelion, elecampane, false unicorn, fennel, fenugreek, galbanum, goldenrod, goldenseal, mistletoe, motherwort, nettles, oregon grape, parsley, peach, peppermint, plantain, pleurisy root, red raspberry, rosemary, shepherd's purse, slippery elm, squawvine, St. John's wort, wild yam, and yarrow.

Many of these herbs are discussed elsewhere in this booklet. Please see the index at the back of this booklet for the page numbers on which each herb is discussed. If you need more information on any of these herbs, consult an alphabetized herbal reference or the web has a wealth of herbal information which is readily available.

Black cohosh The antispasmodic action of black cohosh eases muscle tension and produces natural intermittent uterine contractions during labor. The anodyne and nervine properties of this marvelous herb, which are specific to nerve and muscle pain, make it excellent for labor. Black cohosh is often used as part of a formula to prepare the uterus for the birthing process in the last few weeks of pregnancy.

Black cohosh is used outside of pregnancy to relieve headache, muscle spasms, the bronchial spasms of asthma, and menstrual cramps. Black cohosh is sometimes used to dilate the peripheral blood vessels to lower blood pressure. Black cohosh is strongly anti-inflammatory.

©Copyright Butterfly Expressions, llc 2010   Butterfly Miracles with Herbal Remedies

Blue cohosh is used almost exclusively for things related to pregnancy and childbirth. Like black cohosh, blue cohosh is often part of formulas taken in the last weeks of pregnancy to prepare the woman's body for birth. The relaxant properties of blue cohosh are especially useful when stress and tension are producing uterine irritability, spasmodic false labor pains, and overly strong Braxton-Hicks contractions in the weeks prior to birth.

During labor, black cohosh aids the uterus in producing regular and effective contractions with good rest periods in between. I have seen blue cohosh, in both herbal and homeopathic form, strengthen a labor that is stalling out due to fatigue and uterine inertia. At those times I have breathed a heavy sigh of relief, knowing that we have just averted a likely Cesarean section surgery for mom and baby.

Blue cohosh is often combined with black cohosh; these are complementary plants with similarly beneficial nervine and antispasmodic properties. Combined with other system specific herbs, both cohoshes are used to treat nervous disorders, urinary tract problems, and arthritis.

Chaste Tree stimulates the pituitary gland, particularly in relation to female hormones. The pituitary gland and the ovaries work together to orchestrate the amazing changing of hormones that happens throughout a women's monthly cycle. There are far more hormones involved in this process than just estrogen and progesterone. Because chaste tree communicates with the pituitary it affects all of these hormones to a marked degree. However, chaste tree appears to have more of a progesteronic than estrogenic influence. These properties make it an excellent remedy ro PMS and a whole lot of female problems that are related to too much estrogen in general, or too much estrogen at certain times during the month.

Chaste tree is a good remedy for irregular or painful periods, too heavy bleeding with menstruation, fibroids, and hormone imbalances brought on by contraceptives or inadequate diet. Chaste tree is also a remedy for menopausal problems. It stimulates milk production in nursing mothers and helps them relax and be calm enough to nurse well. In fact, chaste tree's calming and relaxing properties make if effective for any emotional distress associated with the reproductive system, such as PMS and the depression that sometimes accompanies menopause.

Cramp bark is aptly named because it is a remedy specific to cramping pains in the thighs and back, especially if the cramping is accompanied by bearing-down sensations in the uterus. Cramp bark is effective for this type of pain whether it is premenstrual, menstrual, during pregnancy, or during labor and childbirth. Cramp bark is also effective for pain in the legs and back from urinary tract infections.

Cramp bark is used in formulas to prevent miscarriage, and in formulas taken during the last weeks of pregnancy to prepare for labor and birth.

Fennel has been used around the world to increase the production of breast milk. The medicinal properties of the fennel pass to the baby through the mother's milk and soothe any colic or digestive problems the baby may be experiencing. Fennel is also used to regulate the menstrual cycle and relieve the cramping of menstruation.

Fennel contains volatile oils which increase appetite and stimulate the production of digestive enzymes which then increase the absorption of nutrients from the food that is ingested. Fennel relaxes spasms in the digestive tract, relieves gas pains and colic, and often stops hiccups. Fennel is often given to relieve heartburn and the abdominal pain caused by constipation.

©**Copyright Butterfly Expressions, llc 2010   Butterfly Miracles with Herbal Remedies**

Fennel is an excellent diuretic and stimulates the removal of excess water from cells and tissues. Fennel has enough antiseptic action to be useful for kidney and bladder infections. Because it acts against infection and promotes the expulsion of toxins through the urine, fennel is an excellent remedy for gout and kidney stones.

Fennel is a remedy for the improvement of eyesight. It can be used as an eyewash for tired, inflamed, or infected eyes.

Mistletoe is a somewhat controversial herb. Mistletoe is a semi-parasitic plant and its medicinal properties seem to vary a bit according to what plant is acting as its host. Mistletoe has been in use for generations for nervous tension, headaches, insomnia, increasing systolic blood pressure when needed, and controlling uterine spasms and bleeding. Mistletoe also has a strengthening effect on the veins and vascular system.

Mistletoe is controversial because in spite of the long list of things that it is good for, mistletoe contains some rather toxic proteins. Mistletoe should never be taken in large quantities or over long periods of time. Mistletoe seems to go right to work and a dose of a few drops a few times a day for only a day or two is all that is needed. Never take mistletoe night after night for insomnia or day after day for lowering blood pressure.

Mistletoe, taken for 3 or 4 days after giving birth, is an amazing tonic herb. It stimulates the return of the uterus to normal size and tone, but dulls the pain of the contractions that it created for this purpose. Mistletoe should not be taken for any longer than 3 or 4 days at a time for any reason.

I have used mistletoe in the prevention of stroke, and for strengthening veins and arteries in impending stroke situations. Mistletoe is a very valuable herb when used with caution and common sense.

Motherwort is a mild nervine and tonic herb with pronounced hormonal properties. Motherwort is used for painful, delayed, or suppressed periods. It is often used to encourage rhythmic, effective contractions during labor. This stimulating property is offset by strong sedative and relaxing properties and the ability to relieve anxiety and tension. Motherwort is also used in formulas for the prevention of miscarriage.

It has been found that equal parts of motherwort and passion flower make a very good substitute for the expensive and hard to get—impossible at this time—lady slipper.

Motherwort is an excellent cardio tonic. It is used for arrhythmias and palpitations that are brought on by stress, anxiety, and tension. Motherwort will temporarily lower blood pressure, giving a person time to adjust diet and lifestyle to eliminate the problem altogether.

Vervain increases uterine contractions. This aspect of its action makes it useful during labor and birth, but makes it an herb to be avoided during pregnancy. Vervain has diuretic properties and should be used for fluid retention and gout.

Vervain is an astringent with specific action on the liver and gallbladder. Taken as a warm tea, vervain acts as a diaphoretic, producing a sweat that usually breaks a fever. During the convalescent stage of an illness, vervain acts both to increase energy and provide relaxing rest. Vervain is a mild nervine and useful for headaches, migraines, and nervous exhaustion. There are tannins in vervain that are useful astringents for bleeding gums and mouth ulcers. These tannins are also useful for treating wounds and insect bites.

©**Copyright Butterfly Expressions, llc 2010   Butterfly Miracles with Herbal Remedies**

Wild yam has a significant effect on female hormones. Wild yam is traditionally used for easing menstrual cramps because it is strongly antispasmodic. This antispasmodic action makes cramp bark useful for other types of muscular spasms such as colic, flatulence, intestinal and uterine cramping.

Wild yam also contains steroidal saponins which are anti-inflammatory. This combination of anti-inflammatory and antispasmodic properties makes wild yam very important in treatments for arthritis, joint and muscle inflammation, and inflamed bowels.

Wild yam is also a diuretic and nephritic herb. It is soothing to painful and inflamed conditions of the urinary tract.

Wild yam is better used in excitable conditions characterized by some sort of over-stimulation. It is not as appropriate for conditions that are related to lack of tone. Wild yam is specific to cramping and inflammation, particularly when it is related to tension and stress. Wild yam has been used traditionally in many cultures for threatened miscarriage and to relieve the nausea some women experience with pregnancy.

Herbs to Avoid or Use with Caution During Pregnancy

Herbs which stimulate uterine contraction:
Angelica—used after the baby is born to stimulate the expulsion of a retained placenta.
Black and blue cohosh—strong uterine stimulants. Should be avoided during pregnancy, except during the last 4 or 5 weeks when small amounts combined with other herbs can help prepare the mother's body for labor and delivery.
Motherwort and yarrow should be used cautiously, sparingly, and for short periods of time only. They should never be used if a miscarriage is or has been threatened.
Mugwort, nutmeg, pennyroyal, and rue should NEVER be used by a pregnant woman.

Herbs which stimulate bleeding and should be avoided:
Dong quai, motherwort

Other herbs to use cautiously during pregnancy:
Goldenseal—strong hormonal, and sometimes, causes blood sugar levels to spike temporarily. Avoid altogether, use cautiously, or perhaps, substitute oregon grape root. A small percentage of goldenseal in a formula will do no harm; just avoid taking a lot of the single herb during pregnancy.
Horsetail—fine as part of a formula taken for a few days. Other diuretics would probably be a better choice, especially during the first few months of pregnancy. This caution has to do with the high silica content of horsetail.
Licorice root—contra indicated for certain heart conditions, may elevate blood pressure or contribute to water retention in the extremities.
Shepherd's purse—strong astringent, too drying to tissues unless there is bleeding that needs to be stopped.
Mistletoe—has no place at all in pregnancy except to stop bleeding and control pain after a miscarriage.
Uva ursi—useful to stop hemorrhage and tone the uterus after childbirth but should be avoided during the pregnancy itself. Uva ursi is too astringent and drying to use during pregnancy.

©**Copyright Butterfly Expressions, llc 2010   Butterfly Miracles with Herbal Remedies**

Chapter Fifteen
Cathartic Herbal Agents

Cathartics are herbs that cleanse waste matter from the liver, gall ducts, small intestines, and colon. They affect peristaltic action, the secretion of bile, and the nerve impulses to these areas.

The class of herbs which stimulate the evacuation of the bowel are divided into two important and separate categories:

1) agents that cause <u>moderate</u> peristalsis without cramping and irritation, and
2) agents which produce <u>active</u>, or even <u>violent</u>, peristalsis and are accompanied by intense cramping and purging of the bowels.

The herbs listed in books under the general category of cathartics can range from simple laxative to mildly purgative to drastically and uncomfortably cathartic. This should always be taken into consideration.

In the category of moderate herbs, **cascara sagrada** and **aloe vera** (typically used for the large intestine), **licorice** (benefits the entire intestinal tract), and **olive oil** (which has an affinity for the small intestine) are usually included. Many fruits, as well as the drinking of large quantities of water, also have mild laxative effects on the intestinal tract. This category of evacuative herbs is generally recommended for infants, babies, the elderly, or very weak people. The action is usually mild, moderate, and gentle. They are generally most effective when administered at night before going to bed.

The stronger purgative herbs usually accomplish evacuation in a time period of 8 - 12 hours and should be administered in the morning or between meals on an empty stomach. **Cape aloes** (different from aloe vera), **senna** and **turkey rhubarb** are examples of this category. They work predominantly on the large intestine.

It should be emphasized that the purpose of herbal medicines is to bring about normal, healthy function in the body. Treating a condition such as chronic constipation by producing periods of diarrhea between the bouts of constipation is not healthy and does not accomplish anything beneficial in the long run. The gradual softening of the stool and establishment of normal peristalsis should always be the goal. This may require a long-term change in dietary and living habits instead of the taking of an herbal remedy from time to time.

There are herbs available in the wild kingdom that have even more drastic action that the ones listed above. These are extremely irritating and can cause severe inflammation and destruction of delicate membranes and tissues. I can think of no valid reason to use these agents, but if you ever feel the need please be sure to use with emollient and demulcent herbs. Follow up with the demulcents for a long period of time. Much harm has been done to too many people, in my opinion, by the overuse of purging and cleansing methods. I would personally put **castor oil** prominently on this list!! Anything that is strong enough to induce labor (which is what it is sometimes used for) by inducing violent cramping and evacuation of the bowel, is strong enough to think twice about using when pregnant or otherwise!

Other herbs, fruits, and some nuts that are generally listed as stool softening are: **sweet almond, apples, apricots, asparagus, buckthorne, chickweed, chicory, fig, flaxseed, prune, red raspberry, safflower,** and **black walnut**.

©Copyright Butterfly Expressions, llc 2010   **Butterfly Miracles with Herbal Remedies**

Among the herbs that stimulate the flow of bile are **aloe vera, dandelion, goldenseal, hops, licorice, oregon grape root,** and **wild yam**. Stimulating the flow of bile, and thereby, strengthening the digestive and eliminative organs in general, is quite different from purging the bowels.

Herbs which strengthen liver function include **barberry bark, cascara sagrada, dandelion root, gentian, goldenseal, gravel root, horseradish, olive oil, oregon grape, parsley,** and **Turkey Rhubarb.**

You will notice that some herbs appear on more than one list. How the herb works, exactly, depends a great deal on how it is used, when it is used, and what herbs are taken in conjunction with it. Each herb should be studied in detail and thought given to how it combines with other herbs. A few notes on some of the herbs mentioned above are included here.

Cascara sagrada is one of nature's best remedies. It improves the action and general tone of the bowel and does not cause reliance or addiction problems. Some in the herbal world mistake the continued need for the nutrients provided by Cascara sagrada as an unhealthy reliance on the herb, much like the reliance that is sometimes set up by non-herbal laxatives. As long as your diet is not supplying the nutrition needed for proper bowel function, there may be a need for cascara sagrada. It is no more a "dependence" than is the need to eat carrots to obtain beta-carotene. Cascara sagrada is a nutritional/ food type of herb. Please note that cascara sagrada is also listed as liver strengthening and stimulating to the gall-bladder. This is truly a great herb!

Senna is unusual in that it works very promptly—usually within 2 - 6 hours. The action of senna is usually accompanied by cramping, gas, and nausea. These side effects can be greatly minimized by the taking of a little cloves, ginger, cinnamon, coriander, or fennel at the same time as the senna.

Senna should **NOT** be used where there is bowel inflammation, hemorrhoids, or intestinal bleeding of any sort. Monitor this carefully. THIS IS IMPORTANT!! *Large doses* of senna can cause severe vomiting and diarrhea and are generally not recommended. The action of senna is so prompt and thorough that it often creates a form of dehydration in the bowel which results in further constipation. Extra fluids should be taken. Senna does nothing to establish normal function or the presence of healthy bacteria in the colon. Enzymes and acidophilus should be *promptly* added to the diet after senna has been used.

This is a popular herb, especially added to pumpkin seeds, for ridding the body of parasites or general bowel cleansing. You can probably tell from the above description that I am not fond of this idea. I would recommend caution, especially if you are working with children or the elderly.

The addition of **licorice** to bowel formulas modifies (or makes milder) the action of the more drastic cathartic herbs. Licorice is of special benefit to bowel problems that are associated with circulation. An example of such a problem would be hemorrhoids.

Mandrake Root is so potent and so strong that it is easy to misuse. Mandrake should NEVER be given in overdose and should NOT be combined with quick, brisk, or violent cathartics (such as senna). However, mandrake has some special and unusual characteristics which make it valuable in certain circumstances. When given in small, well-managed doses and in conjunction with mild herbs such as licorice or cascara sagrada, mandrake can be very beneficial. Mandrake acts mainly on the duodenum (the connective tissue between the stomach and small intestine). That alone makes it a very valuable and unusual herb. In chronic liver disease, there is probably no better herb any where on the planet. Mandrake's influence and action will continue for hours and sometimes days after use has been discontinued.

©**Copyright Butterfly Expressions, llc 2010   Butterfly Miracles with Herbal Remedies**

Chapter Sixteen
Cardiovascular Herbs

Cardiovascular (heart) herbs come in three varieties: stimulants, depressants, and tonics.

Cardiovascular stimulants increase the power and strength of the heartbeat, and therefore, the pulse. Herbs in this category include: black cohosh, blessed thistle, buchu, **cayenne**, cinnamon, cloves, comfrey, coriander, elecampane, garlic, goldenseal, **hawthorne berries**, motherwort, myrrh, **peppermint**, prickly ash, skullcap, spikenard, valerian, vervain, and wood betony. (Bolding indicates **very** effective herbs.)

Cardiovascular depressants: lobelia, pleurisy root, saw palmetto, valerian, and spikenard.

Note that spikenard and valerian are listed as both stimulants and depressants. That is exactly what they are. If the heart muscle is overexcited, or the electrical signals are misfiring, valerian and its cousin spikenard will calm and re-set the pace. In other circumstances, these two herbs gently stimulate and strengthen while calming irregularities in the pulse and heart rate.

Cardiovascular tonics: angelica, astragalus, comfrey, dong quai, gingko biloba, ginseng, hawthorne, marshmallow, motherwort, mullein, passion flower, rehemania, yucca.

There is a large body of scientific research showing that herbs and nutritional supplements are of value in the treatment of mild to moderate heart disease. There have even been studies in which patients with more severe, chronic heart conditions who were not responding to standard medical treatments, showed marked improvement with herbal and nutritional alternative. Many of these alternative choices are standard medical protocols in Europe and Asia.

Hawthorne is, without doubt, a very important herb for maintaining or rebuilding cardiovascular health. In Germany a government agency, Kommission E, is responsible for setting standards guiding the safe manufacture and usage of herbal medicines. They claim that hawthorne is useful for heart insufficiency because it strengthens heart contractions, lowers blood pressure, and lowers pulse rate. Further, they credit hawthorne with giving the heart increased capacity to continue functioning in low oxygen conditions.

Clinical trials have shown hawthorne to be of benefit with elderly patients with no specific heart conditions except gradually declining heart function overall due to age. A four year study, also done in Germany, found that hawthorne improves contractions in the veins and heart, improves circulation to organs and muscles, lowers blood pressure, improves fatigue and endurance, relieves difficult breathing, and decreases the number of angina attacks. Several Chinese clinical trials have reported that hawthorne lowers cholesterol and triglyceride levels and has a calming effect on the central nervous system.

Cayenne has a long history as a circulatory stimulant and heart tonic and stimulant. Cayenne strengthens the heart, arteries, and capillaries. Cayenne and hawthorne, in equal parts, are my very favorite heart tonic. I added garlic when my own heart was recovering from some pretty serious damage.

©**Copyright Butterfly Expressions, llc 2010   Butterfly Miracles with Herbal Remedies**

Astragalus is well known as an immune tonic. It has also been used traditionally to support the heart. Astragalus lowers blood pressure and increases the hearts endurance when under stress or additional physical activity. Astragalus is particularly effective when combined with **dong quai**. Dong quai is an herbal blood builder.

Ginkgo biloba is recognized the world over for its support of brain function. Ginkgo biloba supports the brain by increasing circulation in the tiniest of blood vessels. Ginkgo biloba works the same way in strengthening the cardiovascular system. Ginkgo is also a powerful antioxidant.

Cactus grandiflorus is used when the heart muscle is enfeebled, where there is progressive valvular inefficiency, and irregular pulse. Cactus has been shown to raise arterial tension, which increases the force and regularity of the pulse. Cactus has a direct influence on the sympathetic nervous system, especially as it relates to the heart. This herb stimulates and strengthens the heart through improved nutrition of the entire nervous and muscular structures related to the cardiovascular system.

I have also successfully used a related plant, yucca, for strengthening the heart and cardiovascular system. Both of these herbs, cactus and yucca, are available as homeopathics and very useful in that format.

BBL, a recipe in the back of this booklet containing lobelia, the cohoshes, vervain, and skullcap is my favorite addition to cardiac protocols. BBL calms and strengthens the heart muscle and the pulse.

©Copyright Butterfly Expressions, llc 2010   Butterfly Miracles with Herbal Remedies

Chapter Seventeen
Miscellaneous Categories

In this chapter we will discuss, briefly, some of the other big words that are often used in books on alternative therapies, and list some of the herbs commonly used in these categories and situations.

Anthelmentic or Vermifuge Herbs

These herbs are used for killing or expelling worms from the body. It should be noted right here at the beginning that the presence of worms in the body is often a sign of overall nutritional depletion, resultant cellular degeneration, and overall poor health. Occasionally the infestation will be recent enough that overall health has not been too badly compromised yet. Parasites require nutrients to live and they use yours to survive and grow on. That is why they are called parasites. Vermifuge herbs must ALWAYS be followed up by a comprehensive program of tonic herbs, good nutrition, and the rebuilding of normal beneficial bacteria in the digestive system.

Some herbs in the vermifuge/anthelmentic category are senna (in large doses), wormwood (sometimes called absinthium), tansy, pumpkin seeds, black cohosh, false unicorn, and hyssop. False unicorn is a mildly anthelmentic herb and should be considered.

Often a tea made with hyssop is the only remedy needed and is much gentler to the system than some of the other alternatives. By their very nature, these herbs can be quite drastic in their effects and care should always be taken. That is not to say that they should not be used—of course there is sometimes a need for a parasite cleanse—but they should be used cautiously and wisely.

A parasite cleanse using Miracle II Neutralizer and a drop or two of the Miracle II Soap, is gentle and effective against most common parasites. Use 1 ounce of neutralizer and 1 drop of green soap once a day for 4 days. Skip one day and repeat the dose. This method does not strip the colon of its normal, healthy bacteria.

Turmeric essential oil can be used, sparingly, for really nasty infestations and for some of the larger parasites.

A note on tansy, which has a reputation for causing abortion. This may very well be so, but obtaining this undesirable effect would require extra large and most discomforting doses. Herbal induced abortions of any kind would almost certainly cause great irritation and destruction to the reproductive system and the intestinal tract! Abortion by herbal means is not a good idea from a health point of view; I will leave the moral aspects of such a plan up to you. Bleeding to death, or causing sufficient destruction to make bearing children in the future unlikely or impossible, is a very real possibility. A lifetime of female problems would almost certainly occur.

Carminative Herbs

By definition, these are herbs that eliminate and expel gas from the stomach and intestines. This is usually accomplished by volatile oils in the herbs that stimulate peristalsis. Gas pains, and their relief by increased bowel and stomach action, are usually spasmodic in nature and quite painful. Antispasmodic herbs taken at the same time can increase the relief supplied and the effectiveness of the carminative herbs.

Some of the herbs commonly used are: angelica root, capsicum (cayenne), caraway seeds, cardamom seeds, catnip, celery seed, chamomile flowers, echinacea, fennel, ginger, hops, lemon balm, parsley root, peppermint, saffron, valerian, and wild yam.

©Copyright Butterfly Expressions, llc 2010   Butterfly Miracles with Herbal Remedies

Emetic Herbs

Herbs which bring about the immediate emptying of the stomach by inducing vomiting. Some emetics, besides emptying the stomach, specifically target the lungs and bronchials, emptying them of mucous at the same time that the contents of the stomach are expelled. Herbs that affect the lungs and bronchials are more often referred to as expectorants.

Severe vomiting, or vomiting for long periods of time can cause dehydration and throw off the balance of electrolytes in the cells and tissues. Repeated or profuse vomiting may cause erosions or small tears in the esophagus. This becomes apparent if fresh red blood is mixed with the vomit. Recurrent vomiting may cause the erosion of tooth enamel and damage to gum tissue. In other words, herbs should not be used to induce vomiting except in rare instances of certain types of food poisoning or flu. Vomiting on a regular basis should never be encouraged.

There are a great many herbs that are listed as emetic herbs. Among them are catnip, elder flowers, false unicorn, ipecacuanha, lobelia, and mustard seed. Most herbs, if given in large enough quantities will induce vomiting. It takes a little less ipecacuanha and lobelia than it does of some other herbs, but that is about the only difference.

Rubefacient

Topically applied, these herbs help to increase the flow of blood and nutrients to the surface of the skin. Increased circulation aids healing and relieves congestion and inflammation in sprains and muscle soreness.

Some herbs commonly used for this purpose include: camphor, cayenne, cloves, eucalyptus, garlic, ginger, horseradish, mustard seed, peppermint oil, pine oil, stinging nettle, and thyme oil. There are, of course, many others.

Many years ago I used to keep some of these herbs tinctured in either alcohol or almond oil to use as liniments for sprains and sore muscles. Then I discovered essential oils. Essential oils, because the volatile oils are still intact, are amazing in this venue and so easy to use.

Vulnerary Herbs

A vulnerary is an herb used to promote the healing of external wounds, cuts, and abrasions. These herbs can be applied as liniments or poultices.

Some useful herbs are: aloe vera, black walnut, burdock, cayenne, comfrey, fenugreek, flaxseed, gentian, goldenseal, hops, horsetail, mullein, oatstraw, plantain, poke root, St. John's wort, spruce, thyme, and yarrow. *Comfrey, plantain, mullein, and yarrow are so phenomenal in this area as to be almost miraculous.*

Arnica flowers must be mentioned for the healing of bruises, but it must be noted that arnica in anything but homeopathic form must be used cautiously on open wounds. Occasionally, arnica can create swelling in open wounds. I don't worry about it much; I just use the homeopathic form if the skin is broken.

Pectoral Herbs

These are herbs that are healing to the broncho pulmonary area—the respiratory system. These herbs are taken internally and/or applied to the chest and back. There is a great deal of lung area well exposed on the back. Sometimes this fact is not taken proper advantage of.

Herbs that are considered beneficial to the lungs and bronchial tubes are: *horehound, coltsfoot, comfrey, elder flowers & berries, elecampane, eucalyptus, fennel, flaxseed, ginseng, hyssop, marshmallow, mullein, onion, peppermint, pleurisy root, slippery elm, spikenard, spruce, yarrow, and yerba santa.*

©Copyright Butterfly Expressions, llc 2010   Butterfly Miracles with Herbal Remedies

Chapter Eighteen
Doing a Cleanse Right

For many years, herbal/alternative medicine has relied on cleanses to restore the body to balance and speed healing. Some of these cleanses can cause pretty severe symptoms and reactions, even the ones that have been in use for many years. Why is it that they seemed to work 50 years ago, but now make people so sick and even seem to do more harm than good in the long run sometimes?

I think that the explanation for this can be found by comparing our world today with the world in which the famous, old-time herbal doctors lived. More and more people today live away from the earth and pollutants and poisons are a part of our every day lives. Chemical fertilizers and weed sprays have increased. We add chemicals to our water and hormones to our meat. And then there are the drugs that most people take so routinely that they often don't even consider them to be drugs any more. I am often amused—and saddened—when I visit the medicine cabinet of a family who has recently gone herbal. Too often it is still full of allergy pills, throat sprays, non herbal cough medicines, pain killers, fever reducers, headache remedies, laxatives, etc.

All of these poisons are pulled out of circulation in the body by the liver. A cleanse, for most people, releases more of these medications than the kidneys and colon can cope with at one time. The result is headache, skin rashes, insomnia, and **the redistribution of the toxins throughout the body.** The poison often chooses to relocate along the brain stem. This contributes to memory and concentration problems. "Doing a cleanse right" means cleaning the liver (and anywhere else that needs it) without this redistribution of the toxins.

A cleanse done with proper supporting herbs should not cause feelings of discomfort while you are doing it. Cleansing shouldn't leave you feeling tired, out-of-sorts, or less than alert when you are finished. The trick here is to balance system cleansing and strengthening efforts in the proper proportions. This can be done easily if one pays attention to the signals the body is sending.

A renowned herbalist, Dr. John Christopher, was fond of saying that **"discomfort" (his polite way of saying downright misery) "will be a sign of carelessness".** Small, frequently repeated doses are more likely to be effective and less likely to cause discomfort.

Toxin Soaks

To aid in the elimination of toxins, drugs, pollutants, etc., from the body, always make toxin soaks a big part of your routine. A whole body soak is the most common way, but personally, I prefer just a foot soak. A whole body soak can sometimes leave you feeling weak and wrung out—even sleepy—for a while.

Toxin soak recipes: **#1**—1 cup sea salt; **#2**—½ cup epsom salts and 1 box of baking soda; **#3**—2 tablespoons of redmond clay (or any diatamaceous earth). Place your choice in a tub of hot water and climb in. Soak for at least 20 minutes, keeping the water as hot as you can. Alternatively, place 2 - 3 T. of clay in a large pan (big enough for your feet) of very hot water. Soak for about 20 minutes, keeping it hot by continually adding hot water as necessary. It is amazing how well pulling the toxins just through the feet works. It is just as effective as the whole body soak, much easier, and doesn't seem to make one feel tired or weak.

I like to routinely add a product called Miracle II Neutralizer to my bath between clay soaks along with whatever essential oils I want at the moment. In this way, I am continually working on the detoxing of my body, instead of going all out only on occasion.

©Copyright Butterfly Expressions, llc 2010   Butterfly Miracles with Herbal Remedies

Water

Drink!! Drink!! Drink!! (Find good water without chemicals, of course, if you possibly can.) This cannot be overemphasized!! Sufficient water will keep the eliminative channels open and prevent a host of discomforting symptoms.

The Cleanse

One good cleanse that I have been using, and recommending, for a long time consists of 5 parts: 1) kidneys, 2) colon, 3) liver, 4) blood, and 5) brain.

It is best to work with the first 4 of the body systems listed above together. All of the systems of the body are dependent on each other; if one is struggling the others usually are too. It is difficult to keep the liver and kidneys functioning well if the colon is continually dumping poisons into the blood stream.

I have made an herbal tincture or two in each of these categories and there are many other good ones on the market. The recipes for the ones I use are in section two of this booklet. I recommend the following:

1) **Kidneys:** KB tincture—or something similar—for the kidneys. Drink, drink, drink (water, of course) and soak, soak, soak.

Other herbs which may be useful: astragalus, buchu, cleavers, cornsilk, cranberries, juniper berries, goldenseal and marshmallow Chapparal is a strong astringent herb and can be useful if there is stringy mucous from the kidneys. Chaparral should be used for only short periods of time. It is helpful to add an emollient such as mullein when chaparral is being taken. Never use chaparral if there is blood in the urine .

2) **Colon:** The CD tincture is a combination that is well balanced between cleanser and support herbs. This is not a dramatic cathartic and stripper. It is used to support the colon and digestive system while the cleanse is proceeding.

Sarsaparilla (see page 63) should be added if you are starting out with a colon that is clogged or malfunctioning in any way.

Support the colon with exercise, mild foods, enzymes, acidophilus, fiber (oat and wheat bran mixture), water, water, water—consistently, every day, no matter what.

Other colon supporting herbs: Aloe vera, buchu, cape aloes, cascara sagrada, cayenne, fenner, ginger, papaya, peppermint, senna. [Using colon herbs in a blend or rotating through them, never using the same one for an extended period of time, is a good idea.]

Essential Oils that may be helpful: LeInside-Out, LeEZ Traveler, peppermint

3) **Liver:** The LC tincture, for the liver, contains both cleansing herbs and tonic herbs to support and strengthen. The essential oils, LeRevitalize and Ledum, may also be helpful.

The liver has a very long list of functions that it performs in the body. One of these functions is the manufacture of carnitine which is essential of cells in the body are going to break down fat—rather than just store it away. Fat accumulates in the cells of the liver first and the liver can store more fat ells that *all* of the other organs combined. If the liver becomes compromised by fat, carnitine is not created and even more fat accumulates. A fatty liver used to be only in alcoholics. That is no longer true. Today's lifestyle and typical dies is a recipe for disaster to the liver.

©Copyright Butterfly Expressions, llc 2010   Butterfly Miracles with Herbal Remedies

What is the problem with a fatty liver? There are many; let me summarize just three of them here.:

1) Fat cells soak up and hold onto toxins. The more fat cells your liver has, the more toxins the liver can hold. Fat cells in the liver uptaking toxins almost sounds like a good thing, until you consider that a large percentage of new red blood cells are "born" in the liver. These new blood cells become contaminated and damaged by the toxins. They then travel throughout the body, trying in their damaged condition to carry oxygen and nutrients to cells and organs, but carrying contaminants instead.

2) Fat cells, in the liver or in the body, store estrogen. When the cells are full, this estrogen spills into the bloodstream. Besides all the nasty symptoms of out-of-balance hormones, estrogen levels which are too high are associated with several types of cancer. Among these are breast and cervical cancers.

3) The liver, magnified under a microscope, looks like a pinkish/red colored filter. If the liver is filled with toxic fat, it cannot do a good job as a filter for the bloodstream.

How common is a fatty liver? In the United States, 15-20% of the general population has too much fat in their liver. Your odds are much higher if you are overweight. Fatty liver can, and does, occur in children.

What are the symptoms of a fatty liver?
- You may be overweight, especially in the abdominal area, and you find it very hard to lose weight.
- You may have elevated cholesterol and triglyceride levels in your blood.
- You may have diabetes type 2.
- You may have been diagnosed as insulin resistant.
- ***You tire easily; in fact, you feel tired all the time.***
- ***You probably have a lowered immune response. You catch everything that comes around.***

Other herbs that may aid the liver: beet root, bilberry, birch seed and leaves, burdock, catnip, dandelion, devils claw, fennel, gotu kola, hawthorne, red clover, thyme, yarrow

4) Blood: RC tincture, which is a blood cleanser and purifier, is an illustration of the synergy of formulas— the sum being better than its individual components. RC pulls toxins, drug residue, fatty cells, etc., out of the blood and makes them available for excretion by the kidneys. RC is also an excellent infection figher.

Other blood cleansing herbs: burdock, cascara sagrada, echinacea, oregon grape root, peach bark, red clover, rosemary, sarsaparilla, and stillingia.

Adjusting the dosage to personal needs

Use the signals that the body sends (or muscle testing, if you do that) to adjust dosages according to personal needs. It is in this adjustment that you are able to keep the cleansing process well balanced. If these four phases of the cleanse are balanced properly, you should be able to avoid nearly all uncomfortable symptoms.

Some example of the need for adjustment:

A frontal headache indicates that too many toxins from the liver are circulating in the blood. It would probably be wise to back off on the LC tincture by taking less at a time and taking it less often for a few days. At the same time, re-emphasize the colon and the kidneys by increasing the KT and CD tinctures and making sure you are getting enough water.

©**Copyright Butterfly Expressions, llc 2010   Butterfly Miracles with Herbal Remedies**

A more general headache, or any dizziness, might be an indication of stress on the kidneys. A possible solution would be to increase the KT and go a little slower on the RC and LC until the kidneys are keeping up with the cleanse again.

An ache in the lower back is another indication that the kidneys are being overwhelmed. Go a little slower, support the kidneys, drink lots of water, and do a toxin soak.

Allergy symptoms, rashes, etc., are almost always a need for more work on the colon. You should have none of these symptoms, or very moderate and of short duration ones, if you are getting the proportion of cleansing herbs right. If you do get symptoms of this sort, simply adjust your program. Be sure to drink more water and do a soak a couple of times a week (at least) until the symptoms disappear.

The Diet

A good diet of simple, nutritious, fairly light, foods is essential at this time. Pay particular attention to the PH balance in the body. It is very important to be alkaline when cleansing. Certain unwanted bacteria cannot exist in an alkaline environment. Good health and balance in the colon can be established during the time of the cleanse, if you pay attention to diet.

Many people recommend a juice fast as part of a cleanse. I have no fault to find with juice fasting for short periods of time except that most people do not like vegetable juices very much. Soon they begin drinking more and more fruit juices and less and less vegetable juices. Fruit juices are sweeter and they feel almost like a treat. Too much fruit juice can create an acidic environment in the body. The result of this unbalanced PH diet and lack of fiber is canker sores, scaly skin, brittle hair and nails, headaches, lack of energy, a runaway candida problem, and a flip-flop between diarrhea and constipation. There are, I am sure, a few other symptoms that I have failed to mention.

What foods are acidic and what foods are alkaline. I have seen many lists and I am not happy with any of them. Acidity and alkalinity is not a black and white thing. You can't say that one food is acidic and another is alkaline. I wish it were that simple, but foods line up all along the PH scale. It is good to know that red meats are more acidic than chicken or fish. Vegetables are *far* more alkaline than fruits. Even among the grains, some are more acidic than others. Oatmeal is quite acidic, but the vitamins that it contains make it worth it—maybe even essential—as a part of the diet..

A good rule of thumb for a diet plan is, in my opinion, to be sure to get plenty of protein with a lot of it coming from plant sources. Consume a lot of vegetables from every color of the rainbow. Add fruits for vitamin C and colon health. Keep an eye on the B vitamins, but don't over do the grains. Most importantly, don't waste any carbohydrates or acidity on sugary stuff if you can help it. Drink plenty of water and get some exercise and sunshine.

5) The Brain

If the cleanse is done too rapidly, particularly from the liver, more toxins begin to circulate in the blood than the kidneys can excrete. The body, knowing that you don't want them in the liver or unable to leave them there because of the liver cleansing herbs being taken, finds new places to put them. Sometimes the body does this by encapsulating the toxins and storing them just under the skin here and there throughout the body. These hard little lumps are called lipomas. The palms of the hands seem to be a particular target for these storage containers.

©Copyright Butterfly Expressions, llc 2010   Butterfly Miracles with Herbal Remedies

The brain and brain stem also frequently become the site chosen to store toxic chemicals, preservatives, and drug residues as they are dumped from the liver. This is particularly common if heavy cleanses have been conducted, in the past, and the kidneys were overwhelmed. Exposure to heavy metals (welding, etc.) or pesticides, weed sprays, and fertilizers can also cause deposits to be made along the brain stem or along the cranial nerves. These deposits can also occur in the joints, within the muscles, or along the nerves anywhere in the body.

Homeopathic detox combinations such as Detox #1 (available at Butterfly Express, llc) can be very helpful here. Any homeopathic detox formula should be started very slowly. Careful monitoring of the kidneys, liver, colon, etc., as you go along and taking advantage of toxin soaks will clear the brain stem and other areas very nicely. Essential oils such as the blends ^{Le}IQ and ^{Le}Focus (Butterfly Express, llc) are also excellent here. *(There are many good homeopathics and essential oils. Most of the Butterfly Express, llc blends were, and still are, my "babies". I know what they were created to accomplish and what they do. They are what I know and love and use, so naturally, they are what I talk about. If there is another line of oils that you know and love, of course you should use them.)*

Essential oils can be helpful all the way through this process in both cleansing, balancing, and rebuilding. It would be helpful to support the endocrine system and the hormones. ^{Le}Endo Relief should accomplish both of these things. ^{Le}Revitalize can help with energy levels and fatigue during the cleansing process.

Rebuilding

Remember to rebuild and strengthen every system. This is a very important step. DO IT!! Some suggested things to use: acidophilus and other live probiotic cultures, enzymes, vitamins, minerals, tonic herbs, emotionally supportive essential oils, etc.

Other tonic herbs: alfalfa, echinacea, ginseng, kelp, nettles.

High Mineral Tea Recipe: equal parts of alfalfa, red clover, dandelion, raspberry, and nettles. I like to add comfrey, hawthorne, horsetail, and oatstraw.

Bee pollen supplements and EPA oils are also very nourishing.

Chapter Nineteen
Conclusion

Most herbs, as you may have noticed in the previous chapters, have more than one major characteristic and fit in more than one general category. One example would be motherwort herb. Motherwort is not even a well recognized herb that everybody is acquainted with and uses, but it is listed in at least ten separate categories—demulcent, diuretic, emmenogogue, nervine, cardiovascular tonic, lithotriptic, alterative, vulnerary, and nutritive. This is true of so many herbs.

The specific action of an herbs whether it is astringent or demulcent, etc., is the first thing to consider. The second thing to understand about an herb is what part of the body the herb has an affinity for. Here, again, many herbs nourish the body as a whole, but many herbs have a particularly strong action on one system or another. This is particularly true of the nervine and tonic herbs.

There is a lot of different herbs out there and a lot of information about many of them in this booklet. There is even more information right at your fingertips through the internet. Don't let the readily available information of our day overwhelm you. Learn to use a few herbs well. Choose an herb or two from each category and for each body system. Make pets of them. Use them frequently until you know them well and you will find your health and the health of your family vastly improved.

Section Two

Recipes

for

Tinctures, Glycerites,
Teas, Poultices, Oils, and Salves

Chapter Twenty
Making Herbal Medicines

The first rule of herbal medicine making is always the same.

"My herbal preparations can never be any better than the quality of the herbs I use."

It is critically important that the herbs you use be of good quality and as fresh as you can get. Wildcrafting, going out into the wild and picking your own, will give you the very best finished products. Of course, this is not always possible. The next best thing is to buy your herbs from a good source.

How do you tell if the herbs you are purchasing are of good quality? A dried herb of good medicinal quality will have a strong aroma and tickle your nose when you smell it. A UPS driver once complained to me about the aroma of the packages he delivered here. I opened the cardboard box and showed him the plastic liner the entire contents were in. Then I showed him the individual foil packages each pound of herbs was packaged in. We opened a bag and examined the lining. He could not believe that he was smelling that "dry old weed" through all that packaging. THAT is a good herb, and a reliable company to purchase from in the future.

Always use an herb in as complete a form as possible. A whole leaf or a cut leaf is preferable to a powder. Powdered herbs are always the last resort. Herbs in powdered form are very vulnerable to light and air. Light and air can destroy the medicinal properties of a powdered herb very rapidly. Never trust a powdered herb unless you just pulverized it yourself from a good quality cut leaf or root. I have found herbal supplements that are already in capsules when I purchase them to be unreliable.

Sometimes capsuled herbs work and sometimes they don't. To get the herb into capsules and into a bottle is quite a process. If during processing, the powdered herb was left in a vat exposed to light and air while waiting to be encapsulated, even for a short time, much of its potency has been lost. The more volatile components have dissipated; and they are gone for good. Taking larger quantities will not give you the medicinal properties that you are need.

Always make your teas and tinctures from herbs in as whole a form as possible; always use herbs that are as fresh as possible. Your final product can only be only as good as the herbs you used to make them.

Potency and Dosage

Inevitably, when I talk about the quality of herbs, the question arises, "If the herb I am using is **very** potent, won't I need to take less of it?" or "If the herb I am using is **very** potent, what will happen if I take too much of it?" The answer to these questions if very simple. Herbs are nutrition. While you can overdose on an herb—of course you can—you would have to work very hard at it and be willing to make yourself quite sick before you slowed down or stopped taking the herb. Herbs are much like vegetables, even the nervine herbs. You might eat more carrots than you need, but you won't usually hurt yourself doing it. The stronger the herb, the sooner you will feel nauseous or chilly and realize that you have had enough. Diarrhea and vomiting will be the next warning, if you miss the earlier ones. You may be miserable but will have done no permanent damage.

©Copyright Butterfly Expressions, llc 2010   Butterfly Miracles with Herbal Remedies

Substitution for Unavailable Herbs

Due to FDA regulations on one hand and over-harvesting of herbs on the other hand, there are some herbs that are no longer available, or are very hard to get, on the world market at this time. But, God is good, and there is more than one herb that will accomplish most everything we need. You will notice that some of the recipes indicate a possible substitution for hard or impossible to get herbs.

Lady slipper

One such herb that will need to be substituted for is lady slipper. It is an endangered species and has not been available in my adult lifetime. Equal parts of motherwort and passionflower make an excellent substitute for lady slipper.

Ma huang

The FDA has issued a ruling making ma huang illegal to sell for medicinal or diet purposes. Most suppliers will not sell, at this time, any member of the ephedra family, not even the very mild brigham tea. These other members of the ephedra family are not on the FDA list, but they are unavailable anyway.

The herbs in the ephedra family are excellent healers when used for a short period of time in recovering from serious illnesses such as pneumonia. They boost energy levels, rev up the metabolism, and stimulate the absorption of nutrients needed for convalescence. They have been used, knowledgeably, for many years in weight loss programs.

Unscrupulous people, with an eye on profits, took ma huang into the laboratory setting and broke it down into its separate components. Then they marketed the metabolism boosting aspects in pill form as weight loss "remedies". In other words, they created a drug product and it had the usual drug side effects!! (Perhaps, we should be kinder and give them the benefit of the doubt and just assume that they didn't know any better, but I doubt it a bit.)

In nature, plants contain trace elements that keep the potent healing effects from being dangerous. Dried herbs and tinctures made from these "whole" plants do not create the side effects that the "drug" forms do.

Ma huang would cause an elevation in heart rate that should be sufficient warning to any sensible person that more than enough had been consumed. This would happen long before any heart damage could possibly result. Even in the drug form, people reported that they felt "wired" and "hyper" when taking it. Their bodies were warning them that this product was probably not good for them. Perhaps they were counting on someone else to protect them and tell them if it was not safe. They got their wish. And now these marvelous herbs are unavailable to the rest of us. I have used ma huang and the other plants in the ephedra family for years with excellent results. I miss them, and I'm sure, I will miss them even more if we ever do get into a real epidemic or crisis situation.

©Copyright Butterfly Expressions, llc 2010   Butterfly Miracles with Herbal Remedies

Methods of Use

Medicinal herbs may be powdered and taken in gelatin based capsules—not my favorite method. They can be made into teas (sometimes called infusions or decoctions). They can also be tinctured. This means that the herbs qre preserved in some liquid medium for use at a later time. Herbs can be made into salves or poultices for external use. Herbs can be simmered slowly over heat and the volatile oils that are escaping into the air inhaled.

Teas:
Some herbs, particularly the diuretics, work especially well when prepared in warm water. The drawback with herbal teas is that many people do not take the time, consistently, to make a tea. Although the tincture may lose a few percentage points medicinally, it is far better for them than an herb that remains in the bag because they didn't get around to making a tea. Instructions for making teas will be given on the next page.

Tinctures:
Fresh or well-dried herbs preserved in a liquid medium for use at a later time are called tinctures. Tinctures are made with alcohol, glycerine, carrier-type oil, and vinegar, on occasion. Tinctures preserve the medicinal qualities of the herbs for long periods of time and they are very convenient. Just add a few drops to water and they are ready to ingest right this minute—no waiting for a tea to steep and no straining. Detailed instructions for making salves and tinctures of all types will be given in subsequent chapters of this section.

Sometimes a carrier oil such as almond oil is used in making a tincture-like preparation. These tinctures are not for internal consumption; they are herbal liniments to be applied externally. These oils would be used for the same purposes as a compress or poultice. I like to poultice an area and then apply an oil liniment between opportunities to sit around with a poultice and a heat pack.

Similar liniments are sometimes made with alcohol, often rubbing alcohol is used because it is less expensive. This is what you are getting when you buy a commercial liniment. Rubbing alcohol is toxic to the body, and it **does** absorb into the body when used as a liniment. If it didn't absorb in, there would be no point in rubbing it on to heal muscles and bones below the surface. This liniment **cannot** be taken internally.

Salves
Herbs processed this way are referred to as "soaked" oils or "protein-based" oils. These oils can be easily made into a salve. The advantage of a salve over a soaked oil is that a salve is not runny. It can be applied more thickly and it stays on longer.

Compress or Poultice:
Place the herb in just enough distilled or filtered water to cover the herb. Bring the mixture barely to a boil, and then remove it from the heat. Let the mixture steep for a few minutes. Take a square of cloth—100% cotton is best, although I often use an old bed sheet—and place the herbs in the center of the cloth. Fold it up so that the herbs will stay inside during use. Place the compress on the body and keep it warm in some manner.

Compresses are used for healing with broken bones, sprains, pulled ligaments, and pain relief. The main purpose of a poultice is to have the healing properties of the herbs applied with warmth and moisture for as long a period of time as possible.

©**Copyright Butterfly Expressions, llc 2010   Butterfly Miracles with Herbal Remedies**

Making Herbal Teas:

Use approximately 1 teaspoon of dried herb, or 2 teaspoons of fresh herb, per cup of water. ***This is only an approximation!*** Different people have differing tastes in the strength of the tea. Bitter herbs do not require a full teaspoon and very intense herbs like cayenne need only a few grains for an effective tea.

1. Use moderately warm water for herbs which contain volatile oils. Herbs containing volatile oils are frequently made from the blossom part of the plant, but not always. Examples of herbs containing volatile oils, which are not entirely blossoms, are peppermint, spearmint, and catnip. Using warm, instead of boiling, water makes a light colored, but extremely potent tea.

2. For most other herbs, bring the water to a boil and pour the water over the herb. Let steep for a few minutes, then strain. Do not put the herb into the water and then bring to a boil. If you do not watch the water/herb mix closely and it comes to a rolling boil, the medicinal properties of the herbs will be destroyed. I like to steep teas with a lid on to preserve as much of the volatile oils and medicinal properties as possible.

3. For roots, place in the water and bring to a boil. Simmer gently for 2-3 minutes. When in doubt, or when making a recipe that contains both roots and leaf herbs, use method #2.

Clear soft rain water, distilled water, or water that has been effectively filtered, makes the best tea. Water without chlorine or other chemicals is absolutely essential for poultices. Chlorine and other chemicals destroy most of the medicinal properties of the any herb. Hard minerals can also interfere with the solubility of some of the nutrients. If the nutrients do not pull out of the herb and into the water, they are not available to you when you drink the water.

Do not leave a tea to steep or simmer in a metal pot. Occasionally, the herb will react unfavorably with the metal. Glass is much preferred. Some people use a drip coffee pot to make tea. The water drips through the herbs, not allowing the tea to steep, but it seems to make a very tasty and quite potent brew anyway. It is an easy, no mess, no fuss method.

Recommended dosage for a tea that you are taking for medicinal purposes is usually one cupful three times per day. If you are drinking herbal teas for the nutritional value, even 1 cup of tea every day would provide many nutrients that we are all missing to some extent or another.

©**Copyright Butterfly Expressions, llc 2010   Butterfly Miracles with Herbal Remedies**

Chapter Twenty-One
Making Herbal Tinctures

The liquid medium into which the herb is placed is call the *menstrum*; the herb is known as the *marc*). For internal use, the menstrum can be alcohol, apple cider vinegar, or vegetable glycerine. A good rule of thumb for beginners is, "When in doubt, use alcohol." The medicinal properties of most herbs are pulled out best in an alcohol tincture.

One hundred proof Vodka (50% alcohol/50% water) is ideal for herbal tinctures, although eighty proof (40% alcohol/60% water) is acceptable for most herbs. When you need to add water to any tincture, distilled or filtered water is necessary.

Some herbs, especially kidney/bladder herbs, do not tincture well in vinegar. The finished tincture looks bad and tastes bad. Some people have reported that these vinegar tinctures make them nauseous. A tincture that is part vinegar and part alcohol is often more palatable. When using vinegar, always use an all-natural apple cider vinegar. Western Family makes one that is excellent and cheaper than the ones in health food stores. It *must not* say "apple cider flavored distilled" on the label.

The proportion of herb (marc) to liquid (menstrum) is known as the weight/volume (w/v) ratio. Standard ratios are:
1. Tinctures of dried, intense botanicals are 1:10. This means 1 part herb, an ounce for instance, to 10 parts liquid, also measured in ounces. Examples of this type of herb are cayenne and the resins such as myrrh and propolis. Most of these herbs require a higher proportion of alcohol to water for maximum potency. I would recommend 50% (100 proof) Vodka.
2. Tinctures of dried, fluffy, absorbent herbs such as mullein, yarrow, hops, etc., should also be 1:10. Always check your tincture after 24 hours to make sure all of the herb is still covered with liquid. Any exposed parts will probably mold and ruin the entire batch.
3. Tinctures of other dried botanicals are made with a 1:8 ratio. For example, if you have 3 ounces of herb you would multiply the 3 by 8 and use 24 oz of whatever liquid you have chosen.
4. Tinctures of fresh plants are made on a 1:3 ratio, if you are using vodka. This is because the plant still contains so much water that the menstrum would become too diluted to pull the herbal properties from the herb. Without sufficient alcohol, the tincture will mold. I have found that a higher ratio of alcohol to water (about 75-80%), and using a 1:4 ration works better. This kind of alcohol is expensive unless you have a source coming out of Mexico. Always use the least amount of alcohol that you feel is effective when making a tincture.

Basic Instructions for Tincture Making:

Measure your herb into a glass jar with a well-fitting lid. Add your menstrum, put on the lid and shake well. Set in a cool place out of direct sunlight—but not "out of sight, out of mind". You will need to shake this concoction at least once per day for 10 -14 days. Add more liquid at any time if the mixture looks dry or if some of the herb is sticking up out of the water. When the 10 -14 days have passed, strain your tincture and discard the herbs.

You can strain a tincture by using an ordinary strainer. This leaves a lot of the menstrum behind. Straining the herbs through a cheesecloth works well, but is messy and stains your hands badly unless you wear gloves. This also leaves quite a lot of the menstrum still clinging to the herb. A centrifugal juicer, such as the JuiceMan or the Omega, work very well. You will get back nearly all of your expensive alcohol, vinegar, or glycerine.

©Copyright Butterfly Expressions, llc 2010   Butterfly Miracles with Herbal Remedies

A tincture stored in a cool place in a glass jar will keep indefinitely, remaining as potent as the day you made it. Evaporation is the major enemy. Tinctures need to be watched closely and have the lids changed regularly. This is especially true of vinegar tinctures. Use a plastic lid, rather than a metal one, if possible.

Glycerite Tinctures:

For making herbal glycerite tinctures, it is recommended that you use non synthetic vegetable glycerine.

Glycerine has the capacity to break down and remove certain chemicals and preservatives from the body. It is an excellent medium for herbal tinctures. The sweet flavor makes it especially appropriate for children. When diluted, glycerine is demulcent, emollient, soothing, and healing. Undiluted, it is an irritant and a stimulant and difficult to use because it is so thick. Glycerine tinctures do not have the indefinite shelf life that alcohol tinctures do.

In almost all glycerine tinctures, you will need to dilute the glycerine to a 60% glycerine/40% water solution. Distilled or filtered water is best. In other words, if you need 10 ounces of liquid for your tincture, you would mix 6 ounces of glycerine with 4 ounces of water.

A word of caution: some books will tell you that 50% glycerine/50% water solution is good enough. Experience has shown me that this is not always the case. 60% to 70% glycerine is more reliable. If some alcohol is tolerable, 10% added to 50% glycerine/40% water formula is ideal. The alcohol acts as an additional preservative.

A few drops of an essential oil called benzoin added to the finished and strained glycerite at a ratio of 4 drops to each 8 cups of tincture is helpful. The benzoin does not interfere with the medicinal properties and greatly improves the length of time the tincture can be stored. In fact, benzoin has some good medicinal qualities of its own. A glycerite without alcohol or benzoin has a shelf life of 1 to 3 years. Benzoin adds at least an additional 2 or 3 years to the time the tincture can be stored and still be an effective remedy.

On occasion glycerite tinctures are applied topically to help keep skin surfaces moist. Glycerine does not evaporate at either body or room temperature, and it produces a sensation of warmth to the skin or the tongue. Glycerine is very emollient and is useful for really tough dry skin problems. Glycerin is quite sticky, and since it does not evaporate, can be a little bit annoying for a few minutes until it absorbs into the skin.

Skin rashes that are caused by a bacterial or fungal infection should be treated using the herbs in tea form. Glycerine and carrier type oils provide "food" for the fungus and may actually make the condition worse.

Making a Glycerite Tincture:

Use a 60% glycerine, 40% distilled water menstrum (as described above) and a ratio of from 1:8 to 1:10. This means that you will use 8 - 10 ounces of menstrum (combined glycerine and alcohol) for each 1 ounce of herb. Stir the glycerine and water together thoroughly first. Then place herb and liquid in a canning jar. Place a tight lid on the bottle and cold pack can it, much like you would do for fruit. The water need only come to the neck of the jar. Leave in the canner with the water lightly boiling for 2 hours. Remove the jar from hot water and wait for it to cool. You will need to take off the lid a couple of times while it is cooking so that you can stir the mixture. Try to get all of the herb under the liquid as soon as possible.

©Copyright Butterfly Expressions, llc 2010   Butterfly Miracles with Herbal Remedies

I have done this with a variety of herbs, including peppermint, and the heat does not destroy the medicinal properties of the herbs at all. Glycerine is a heavy medium, even diluted, and with a tightly fitting lid the medicinal properties cannot dissipate into the air. Tinctures made this way are very potent and effective. In making peppermint tea, perhaps the loss of the volatile oils and their properties is due to diffusion into the air rather than destruction by heat. Perhaps we should make all our teas with lids on them.

Glycerites (glycerine tinctures) have the added advantage of being ready to use in a few hours instead of in two weeks. This can be a very great advantage.

***Note: Wild Cherry Bark cannot be heated under any conditions. Note in the Wild Cherry Cough Syrup Recipe that the Wild Cherry is placed in the glycerine/water mixture 24 hours before the batch is going to be processed. It is simply allowed to sit. It is not heated with the rest of the ingredients. Strain the wild cherry bark when you strain the rest of the batch and mix them together.

Tincture Dosages

An alcohol tincture is taken, 12 to 20 drops in a little bit of water. It is usually advisable to take tinctures along with a meal. The nutrients are more likely to be absorbed that way. With something in your stomach, the tincture will be less likely to cause an upset tummy. Depending on the severity of the problem, tinctures should be taken 2 to 5 times a day.

Tinctures are administered in drops, and at least half of those few drops are just water if you used Vodka to make the tincture. The alcohol consumed when taking an herbal remedy is negligible. It is far less than that contained in over the counter remedies such as Benedryl and children's cough syrups. In fact, you will be consuming less alcohol taking herbal remedies that you consume when adding vanilla to your favorite frosting recipe.

Alcohol dissipates very rapidly with heat. Since you will be adding the tincture to a couple of tablespoons of water to take it anyway, just make sure the water is very hot when you put the tincture into it. The alcohol will dissipate instantly. You will have completely eliminated the alcohol with this simple step.

Making an Infused Oil Liniment:

Infused oils are made much like an alcohol tincture. Place herbs in oil (almond or olive or whatever you choose) using a 1:8 ratio. Cover with cheesecloth (or something similar) and let sit in a warm place for 10-14 days. The mixture should be shaken or stirred often. When the 14 days have passed, the mixture should be strained much like an alcohol tincture. It is best to cover the jar with a cloth rather than a tight lid. A little air flow keeps the oil mixture from molding. When using fresh plants, let the plants wilt for 4-8 hours before placing in the oil. This eliminates some of the moisture that might cause mold. Adding 2 drops of benzoin essential oil to each 3-4 cups of oil will also help prevent mold from forming and give the oil a longer shelf life.

Fresh plants for tinctures or oils are far superior to dried ones. The peak harvesting time varies greatly from plant to plant, making harvesting different plants very inconvenient. One plant oil that is much better made with fresh flowers is arnica; the dried flowers do not have the same potency as the flowers when fresh. Arnica grows in our area. Most years it is ready for harvest by the end of June. Rosehips are another herb that should be harvested fresh, if possible. They are mature when they turn red. This will occur after the first hard frost.

©Copyright Butterfly Expressions, llc 2010   Butterfly Miracles with Herbal Remedies

Chapter Twenty-Two
Recipes

It is difficult to measure less than 1/4 ounce of an herb. Even with 1/4 ounce being used for some of the parts, a few of these recipes are quite large because there are so many different herbs used to make them. Do the math, adjusting according to how much tincture you wish to have when you are finished. Just do the best you can with the little trace of some herb that will then be called for.

COMBINATION	INGREDIENTS	COMMENTS AND COMPANIONS
ABF formerly Afterbirth Formula	2.00 cramp bark 1.00 catnip 0.50 motherwort 0.50 skullcap 0.50 yarrow flower or herb 0.50 St. John's wort	To be used for the pain of after-birth contractions. *Use VIB tincture and/or angelica essential oil for release of the placenta. ^{Le}Millenia essential oil applied to the abdomen after birth will help the uterus firm up and prevent bleeding. Be sure to wait to apply ^{Le}Millenia until the placenta has delivered.*
AC formerly Acne	2.50 buchu 1.50 burdock root 1.50 dandelion root 1.50 hyssop 1.00 alfalfa 1.00 chapparal 1.00 red clover blossoms 1.00 uva ursi 0.50 yellowdock root 0.25 cayenne 0.25 plantain	This formula for acne problems is meant to cleanse the kidneys, liver, and blood. Good diet is essential and a liver cleanse with olive oil or with the LC (Liver Cleanse) formula may help. Be sure to support the kidneys and the bowel function, perhaps using the KB (Kidney Bladder) and LB (Lower Bowel) formulas. Acne is often the result of the body using the skin to eliminate toxins because the kidney and colon are clogged. Average dose is 10-20 drops 2 to 4 times a day. Be sure to drink lots of water.
AD formerly Adrenal Toner	2.00 licorice root 1.00 astragalus 1.00 ginseng root 0.50 ginger root	Helpful for chronic fatigue and mononucleosis *(use with full program (ask me or look in Level One Homeopathy booklet). The full program includes adrenal support homeopathics, additional tinctures, and some supplements.*
AL formerly Allergies	2.00 nettles 2.00 yerba santa 1.00 propolis 1.00 gingko biloba 1.00 licorice root 2.00 ephedra or substitute for ephedra 1.00 motherwort 0.50 red clover blossoms 0.50 golden rod	Take a dropperful 3 times a day. *Begin with lots and lots of vitamin C for the acute attack. Start taking bee pollen about February. Nothing will really work well as long as you are still eating a predominantly acidic diet.* *Homeopathics: Allergies #1, Allium cepa and Apis meliflica, or whatever deep level homeopathic that tests for the specific instance and allergy, should be taken.*

©**Copyright Butterfly Expressions, llc 2010   Butterfly Miracles with Herbal Remedies**

COMBINATION	INGREDIENTS	COMMENTS AND COMPANIONS

APL

formerly
Anti-Plague
(antviral)

These are the
same herbs
as the BHM
formula, but
the processing
method is
different.

2.00 comfrey root
1.00 lobelia
1.00 marshmallow root
1.00 mullein leaves
1.00 skullcap
1.00 uva ursi
1.00 white oak bark
1.00 wormwood
0.50 black walnut hulls
0.50 black walnut leaves

Use for viral flu and pneumonia and as a preventative.

To make: tincture herbs in apple cider vinegar (about 1 quart for each 4 ounces of herbs) for 2 weeks, shaking daily, then strain. Peel 1 lb 4 oz of garlic. Blend garlic with enough vinegar to make a thick soup. Tincture the garlic for the same 2 weeks, shaking daily, strain. Mix herb and garlic mixtures into 3 cups vegetable glycerine and 2 cups honey. Makes about 1 gallon.

Dosage is 1 teaspoonful at least 3 times a day.

ARN
Arnica Flower
Oil

place flowers in oil, cover with a loose-weave cloth. Let set 2 weeks. Strain. *Fresh flowers are best.*

Useful for bumps, bruises, and swelling. ***External use only!*** Do not put on open cuts or deep scrapes. Arnica homeopathic may be used internally or applied to those types of areas.

AP

formerly
Arthritis
Plus

2.00 yucca
1.00 white willow bark
1.00 hydrangea
1.00 devils claw
1.00 alfalfa
1.00 burdock root
0.50 black cohosh
0.50 sarsaparilla root
0.50 prickly ash
0.50 slippery elm bark
0.25 cayenne
0.25 licorice root
0.25 pau d'arco bark
0.25 parsley root
0.25 parsley leaves
0.50 kelp

This tincture provides many of the trace minerals needed by the body. It is very good for inflammation of any kind. It can be made into a salve which works very well for some forms of arthritis, for sports injuries, and bone spurs.

ASP

formerly
Antispasmodic

1.00 lobelia
1.00 skullcap
0.50 black cohosh
0.50 blue vervain
1.00 oregon grape root
0.50 cayenne
1.00 wild yam

Useful for muscle cramps, charley horses, mild seizures, coughs, and muscle spasms. Excellent used externally as a liniment. Sometimes the lungs need to expel mucous. In that case, you can use it to help the patient rest for brief periods when exhausted, but use an expectorant during the day to prevent the lungs from filling with fluid. WC (wild cherry cough syrup is a wonderful combination of soothing and expectorant properties. For external use as a muscle relaxant, you can tincture this in wood alcohol and use as a liniment. Be sure to label accordingly as "not for internal use". Much less expensive!

©Copyright Butterfly Expressions, llc 2010   Butterfly Miracles with Herbal Remedies

COMBINATION INGREDIENTS

COMMENTS AND COMPANIONS

BAC

formerly
Bacteria

0.50 cayenne
2.00 echinacea root
0.50 lobelia
0.50 oregano
1.00 oregon grape root
0.50 pau d'arco
1.00 plantain
1.00 red clover blossoms
1.00 usnea

BAC is particularly good for some of the nasty new strains of bacteria that are going around these days. BAC should be used in conjunction with IF—Infection Fighter, RC—Red Clover Combination, other infection fighting herbs, essential oils, and homeopathics for best results. This is true of all tincture formulas!

BBL

formerly
B&B

*please see
page 113
for more
information
about BBL*

1.00 black cohosh
1.00 blue cohosh
1.00 blue vervain
1.00 skullcap
0.50 lobelia

Use much like ASP (antispasmodic). Particularly helpful for healing and relieving the pain of ear infections. Use 3 to 5 drops in the ear with 3 to 5 drops of garlic or mullein oil (soaked oils, not essential oils) for infection. Place a bit of cotton ball in the ear after applying the tinctures. Also useful for coughs, bronchitis, asthma conditions, uterine and pelvis problems, insomnia, headaches (back of head at base), high blood pressure, heart palpitations, and the onset of colds. BBL is especially calming for children. For internal use 10-20 drops is generally used. Use 20-40 drops in the tub for relaxation and pain relief.

BC

formerly
Bowel
Cleanser

2.00 cascara sagrada
1.00 bearberry (uva ursi)
1.00 cayenne
1.00 fennel
1.00 ginger root
1.00 oregon grape root
1.00 lobelia
1.00 red raspberry leaves
1.00 turkey rhubarb root
0.50 myrrh

Use to loosen old fecal matter and clean the bowel. It is very effective if used as part of a complete cleanse with moderate fasting, enemas, herbal food, clay/psyllium husk drinks, and good enzyme/bacteria replacement. Use 2-6 capsules morning and night.

BHM

Bone
High Mineral

formerly
BFC

same dry herbs as in the APL formula, but made into a regular tincture and used differently.

This should tell us something about the role of nutrition and nutritive herbs in the relieving of diseased states.

Use as a mineral supplement, especially for calcium and magnesium. Helpful with teething babies and the healing of breaks, sprains, and burns. Same herbs as APL except for garlic—and indication of the part nutrition plays in relief of diseases. Use with nervine herbs and essential oils for depression.

These same herbs are used in the salve recipe of the same name.

©**Copyright Butterfly Expressions, llc 2010   Butterfly Miracles with Herbal Remedies**

COMBINATION	INGREDIENTS	COMMENTS AND COMPANIONS

BP

formerly
Blood
Pressure

1.50 gotu kola
0.50 brigham tea
2.00 shepherd's purse
1.00 osha
1.00 dandelion root
 .25 cayenne
(1.0 ma huang)

substitute for ma huang
 .50 red clover blossoms
 .25 chapparal.
 .25 golden rod

If brigham tea is not available, increase golden rod to .5 and add .25 of wood betony

BP has been used for many years and by many people to reduce high blood pressure. Most people were able to eventually maintain optimum blood pressure reading without medication. HVC or cayenne needs to be included in the daily regimen.   A diet which includes lots of fresh vegetables—especially green ones is essential. Improving the diet <u>always</u> improves the chance of good results! A moderate exercise program is also recommended.

The original formula called for 1 part ma huang, which is no longer available.

BRON

formerly
Bronchitis

1.00 yerba santa leaf
1.00 osha root
1.00 usnea
1.00 lomatium root
1.00 pau d'arco
1.00 echinacea root
0.50 oregon grape root
0.50 propolis (if available)
 .50 licorice root
 .50 elecampane

BRON is useful for bronchitis and mild pulmonary and respiratory congestions. It is best to use one of the infection fighters (IF, RC, BAC, etc.) along with this formula.

BRON should be used with PL if there is any indication of pleurisy (inflammation in the membrane surrounding the lungs). If you have pleurisy, it will hurt to inhale (may just plain hurt)

CAC

2.00 burdock
2.00 buckthorn
1.00 licorice root
1.00 red clover blossoms
1.00 uva ursi
1.00 poke root
1.00 senna

CAC has a laxative effect on the bowels. Use as a tea for cleansing and purifying the body and the blood.
Instructions:
Mix 1/2 cup of herbs with 1 quart distilled or filtered water. Bring to a boil, then simmer for 45 minutes. Strain.   Add the same herbs that you just strained to another quart of fresh water. Bring to a boil and simmer for another 45 minutes. Strain. Mix the two liquids. ***Dosage is 4 - 12 ounces once or twice a day.*** Don't know why the method is as it is, but those are the instructions I was given. ***Excellent stuff—but very potent.***

CAN

formerly
Candida

2.00 echinacea root
1.00 lobelia
2.00 red clover blossoms
0.50 thyme
1.00 usnea

CAN is meant to be taken internally to aid in fighting an overgrowth of *Candida Albicans* or any other bacteria which produce similar symptoms.

©Copyright Butterfly Expressions, llc 2010   **Butterfly Miracles with Herbal Remedies**

COMBINATION   INGREDIENTS   **COMMENTS AND COMPANIONS**

CART

formerly
Cartilage
Formula

3.00 white oak bark
2.00 alfalfa
1.50 thyme
1.00 dandelion root
1.00 red raspberry leaf
0.50 fo-ti

For the repair and rebuilding of cartilage in the back or knees. Determine before using this formula if you have a fused or compressed disk or other damaged cartilage. If so, use red clover (single herb—not the RC combination) to separate and repair them. White oak bark can be helpful here, as well as the BHM (Bone High Mineral) formula. Damage in disks or bones will break down the new cartilage as rapidly as it forms. KNA is also of great value here. LeMillenia and LeDeeper (essential oil formulas) should be applied at least twice daily in addition.

Cayenne

Tincture using 1:8 ratio and alcohol that is 100 proof or higher. Use fresh or whole dried cayenne peppers.

Useful for bleeding, shock, poor circulation, blood clots, and so much else. Use 10-30 drops every few hours as needed, or use in HVC (most effective).

Cayenne Hawthorne

2.00 hawthorne berries
1.00 cayenne peppers

Tincture using 1:6 ratio and alcohol that is 100 proof or higher. Use fresh or whole dried cayenne peppers.

Strengthens heart and circulation. Use 15-30 drops 2-3 times a day. Add 1 part mistletoe or take mistletoe in conjunction with this formula for better circulation to extremities. **Do not take mistletoe for extended periods of time. (More than 2 or 3 weeks.)**

CC

formerly
Children's
Compound

1.00 yarrow herb or flowers
1.00 elder flower
1.00 peppermint
1.00 mullein leaf or flowers
1.00 red clover blossoms

First response for flu symptoms, colds, and fevers. Perfectly balance to be effective against bacterial, fungal, and strep infections. Rids the body of excess mucous. This is one of the great ones—even for adults. *Make as a glycerite*

Catnip Chamomile

equal parts of
catnip
and
chamomile

This one is always made as a glycerite because it is typically used for colicky, cranky or teething, cranky children. Excellent for adults with bloating and/or gas and for those who are having trouble sleeping.

CB

formerly
Cramp
Bark
Formula

(menstrual)

1.00 cramp bark
1.00 chaste berries
0.50 ginger root
0.50 false unicorn
0.50 passion flower
0.50 motherwort
0.50 cayenne
0.50 squawvine
0.50 white birch bark
0.50 wild yam
.25 black cohosh
.25 blue cohosh

Useful for menstrual cramping and is particulary effective when used with BBL tincture and LeWoman Wise essential oil. Often BBL, alone, is sufficient to relieve menstrual cramping.

©Copyright Butterfly Expressions, llc 2010   Butterfly Miracles with Herbal Remedies

COMBINATION INGREDIENTS	**COMMENTS AND COMPANIONS**

CD

formerly
Colon
Digestive

0.25 lobelia
1.00 oregon grape root
2.00 cascara sagrada
4.00 slippery elm bark
3.00 marshmallow root
3.00 plantain leaves
1.00 chamomile flowers
1.00 elecampane
0.50 papaya

For inflammation and irritation in the digestive tract; chronic indigestion/colitis/ulcers of the small intestine, and constipation. Effective as a colon cleanse—use 3 or 4 times a year. Be sure to support the liver and the kidneys. KB, LC, RC, and this one make a good all around cleansing program.

Use 15-20 drops every 2-4 hours as needed.

CF

formerly
Chronic
Fatigue

2.00 lomatium
1.00 astragulas
1.00 osha
2.00 echinacea root
0.50 goldenseal or oregon
        grape root
1.00 ginseng root
2.00 licorice root
1.00 usnea

Use with AD (Adrenal Toner), homeopathics, supplements, and other tinctures mentioned with AD. Often useful to add the MH (Men's Herbs) tincture from time to time also. There are many good herbal combinations for symptoms similar to chronic fatigue listed in the Homeopathic Combinations booklet also produced by Butterfly Expressions, llc.

Cascara Juniper

equal parts of
cascara sagrada
    and
juniper berries

Use with RM (Raspberry/Myrrh) to strengthen the pancreas and stabilize blood sugar fluctuations.

COL

formerly
Colic
(for adults or
children)

1.00 catnip leaves
1.00 fennel seeds

I like to make this one as a glycerite.
Use for colic, gas, and stomach pain. Use 3-4 drops for babies, 10-20 drops for older children.

CCH (/Chamomile) is equally as effective and not as strong as fennel for children.

COLA
formerly
Colic
Formula
(for adults)

1.00 catnip
1.00 peppermint
1.00 yarrow
1.00 lobelia

This can be made as a tea or a tincture. Sipping a warm tea, however, can be especially soothing during an attack of gallstones. The PPAC formula made into a poultice and placed over the gallbladder area brings a measure of relief. Celestial Seasoning's Tension Tamer or Sleepytime teas are also excellent in conjunction with this formula.

©Copyright Butterfly Expressions, llc 2010   Butterfly Miracles with Herbal Remedies

COMBINATION INGREDIENTS   **COMMENTS AND COMPANIONS**

COMP   2.00 white pine bark   First response for colds, sore throats, and viruses,
                4.00 bayberry   particularly in the head. *Dosage: 15-20 drops every*
formerly   2.00 ginger root   *2-3 hours.* Add infection fighting formulas (such as
Herbal   1.00 cinnamon bark   IF, FN, and SS) if strep throat is suspected. The SN
Composition   1.00 cloves   (Sinus) formula can also be helpful.
                1.00 astragalus
                2.00 elderberries   Also for use during the last week of pregnancy to help
                0.50 cayenne   stimulate the uterus to action. Seems odd, I know, but
                                           it really does work!

CR   0.50 cayenne   Another good first response for sore throat, etc.
                0.50 lobelia
formerly   0.50 prickly ash
Crisis   1.00 blue vervain
                1.00 black cohosh

EB   1.00 mullein   **Not for use as a tincture!**
                2.00 oregon grape root   Useful for pink eye, infected tear ducts, etc. Make tea
Eyebright   1.00 goldenseal leaves   with 1 Tablespoon of herbs per cup. Strain very well.
Formula   1.00 raspberry   Use 2-8 drops in the eye, or use an eye cup at least
                2.00 eyebright or   twice a day. Use more frequently if infection is very
                        passion flower   bad. Treat both eyes to prevent spreading to the other
                                           eye.   Burns the eye a bit—usually according to how
                                           much infection there is!

EO   approximately   Combine all ingredients and cover with a soft cloth.
                6 cups olive or almond oil Let stand for 10 days. Stir the mixture at least once
Ear Oil   1 oz vitamin E oil   each day. Strain.

                1 oz calendula flowers   Use for ear infections by placing 3-5 drops in the ear
                1 oz willow bark   along with 2-3 drops of BBL tincture. Then place a
                1 oz usnea   small piece of cotton in the ear. Use with an infection
                1 oz mullein flowers   fighting formula of some kind and some rosehip tea or
                1 bud—not clove—of garlic tincture for extra vitamin C.
                  or 9 drops garlic essential
                oil added after straining. *Can also be made from oils that you have made with*
                                           the fresh herbs during the season. Excellent!
                The oils listed in the second
                part above are not essential
                oils.   They are vegetable
                oils similar to other carrier
                oils.

©Copyright Butterfly Expressions, llc 2010   Butterfly Miracles with Herbal Remedies

COMBINATION	INGREDIENTS	COMMENTS AND COMPANIONS

ESS

similar to
the famous
Essiac
tea

8.00 burdock
8.00 sheep sorrel
2.00 slippery elm
0.50 turkey rhubarb
2.00 red clover blossoms
1.00 watercress
1.00 blessed thistle
1.00 kelp

DO NOT USE IF PREGNANT/NURSING

This is the strongest cleanser that I know of. Needs to be used 8-20 drops 2 times a day on an empty stomach. It is recommended that no food be eaten 2 hours before or after each dose.

Commonly used as a tea. Reduce recipe for making a tincture.

EUST

Eustachian
or
Red Root
Cleavers
Formula

2.00 usnea
   (can use 3 parts red root)
2.00 cleavers
3.00 mullein leaves or
      flowers
1.00 nettles
1.00 horsetail
1.00 sage
1.00 oregon grape root
0.50 poke root
0.50 ginger root
1.00 red root, if desired

This is a great eustachian, ear, and sinus formula. I have had two people display an allergic reaction to the red root—both were very miserable. I now use usnea instead of the red root. Usnea does not have the lymph draining properties of the red root, but is a great strep and fungal fighter. The mullein, poke root, and cleavers contained in this formula are more than sufficient to accomplish the necessary lymph draining.

EW

formerly
Energy/
Weight Loss

1.00 brigham tea
1.00 red clover blossoms
0.50 chaparral
0.50 golden rod
1.00 dandelion root
2.00 kelp
0.50 mustard seed

2.0 ma huang was in the original recipe with dandelion, kelp, and mustard. The other ingredients are substitutes for the ma huang.

Ma huang is no longer available—substitute brigham tea, red clover, chaparral, and goldenseal in the proportions indicated. If no brigham tea is available, increase the proportions of the red clover, chaparral, and goldenseal.

Provides stimulants to up the metabolic rate, diuretics to shed excess water, and iodine for better thyroid function.

Should not be taken for extended period of time. About 6 months should be the maximum.

EZ

formerly
Eczema

1 pt burdock seed, crushed
1 pt sunflower seed,
   crushed

Steep herbs 10-15 minutes, strain. Drink 1 cupful 3 times daily. Best if used with a good topical cream or essential oils. Cleaning the colon and supporting the kidneys is also essential.

©Copyright Butterfly Expressions, llc 2010   **Butterfly Miracles with Herbal Remedies**

COMBINATION INGREDIENTS

COMMENTS AND COMPANIONS

FC

formerly
Flu
Combination

0.50	bayberry
0.50	ginger root
0.50	cloves
0.50	cayenne
0.50	oregon grape root
1.00	licorice root
1.00	white pine

A good formula for flu strains, whether affecting the stomach or the lungs. If the lungs are being affected, consider LCON and PL for use with this formula.

Can use goldenseal or myrrh for the oregon grape.

FN

formerly
Anti-Fungal
or
Pau d'Arco
Usnea

2.00	pau d'arco
2.00	usnea
1.00	black walnut leaf
1.00	calendula flowers
1.00	echinacea root
0.50	oregon grape root
0.50	myrrh

Take internally as a tincture to fight infection. It would probably be best used as a strong tea when soaking body parts such as the feet for athlete's foot; an alcohol tincture applied topically would sting and irritate and an oil or glycerine based tincture would feed the fungus, making things worse.

Can substitute goldenseal for oregon grape.

FS

formerly
Flu Stopper

consider the homeopathic version

2.00	licorice
2.00	sweet cicily or lomatium
1.00	ginger root
0.50	oregon grape root
0.50	cayenne

This is a really good, effective formula!!
More often than not this remedy will cause the person to vomit once or twice rather violently, but a little while later they will feel much better. They might even wonder if they were really coming down with the flu at all. Works well for indigestion caused by overeating or eating too many rich foods.
Can use goldenseal or myrrh for oregon grape.

FSW

formerly
Five/Six
Week
Formula

Polly/Jeanne

1.00	blessed thistle
1.00	blue cohosh
1.00	false unicorn
1.00	red raspberry leaves
1.00	squawvine
.25	bayberry
.25	lobelia
.25	motherwort
.25	wild ginger (canada snake root)
.25	wild yam

For use in preparing mother and baby for the upcoming birth. Take last 6 weeks of pregnancy. *Use 6 drops for the first week, 8 drops second week, 10 drops third week, then 12 drops until due date. This dosage is taken twice a day.* Really does make a difference to the length of an otherwise normal labor.

FV

formerly
Fever

1.00	elder flowers
1.00	peppermint leaves

Causes perspiration and lowers fever. Use 15-30 drops every 2-3 hours. Never suppress a fever in any other way than by bringing about a good sweat. *Usually made in glycerine, especially when using with infants and children. These two herbs pull very well in glycerine, and would be appropriate for adults also.*

©Copyright Butterfly Expressions, llc 2010   Butterfly Miracles with Herbal Remedies

COMBINATION	INGREDIENTS	COMMENTS AND COMPANIONS

Gingko Dong Quai

equal parts of
gingko biloba
and
dong quai

Useful for improving memory and concentration. Seems to rebuild neural pathways in the brain. Helps to prevent minor strokes that occur in some people as they age.

GI

formerly
Gallstone
Indigestion

2.00 yarrow leaf or flower
1.00 gentian
1.00 papaya
0.50 cape aloes
0.50 angelica root
1.00 oregon grape root
1.00 slippery elm bark
1.00 dandelion root

This tincture is particularly effective taken about 15 minutes before you know you are going to eat things that don't agree with you. For gall bladder sufferers, take 15 minutes before every meal. It notifies the gall bladder to produce and distribute bile. Made up of great herbal bitters. Others could be substituted. Eventually, in a month or two, olive oil/lemon juice cleanse with lobelia or essential oil pain pack on abdomen will need to be done to rid the body of gallstones altogether. This program should be followed by mild food and herbs to rebuild the ducts that may have been damaged as the gall stones were passed.

Ginger Bath

3 T. ginger powder or
      20-30 drops tincture
Follow basic tincturing instructions.

Mix powder or tincture in tub of hot water and soak 30 minutes or more. Relaxes tired or overworked muscles. Stops early labor by increasing oxygen to uterus, allowing it to relax. Increases labor at term if it has slowed due to maternal fatigue or tension.

At the onset of any illness, a ginger bath will increase circulation and body temperature, effectively killing bacteria, virus, and fungal infections. Be sure to wrap up warmly and sweat for at least 30 minutes after the bath, being careful not to get chilled.

Green Drink

dandelion leaves
marshmallow leaves
grasses
redroot leaves
plantain
parsley
wheatgrass
peppermint, spearmint
spinach
swiss chard
shepherd's purse
beet tops
stinging nettle
comfrey leaves
alfalfa
catnip
yellow dock (a little)

One of the best supplements I know of. Make with freshly picked, young, tender leaves. Use as many varieties as you can find. Wash herbs well. Blend with water. Strain. Add pineapple, apple, or orange juice and some honey (if desired). Drink 2-4 cups daily. Grow and juice wheatgrass when fresh herbs not available. Spinach, beet tops, and greens from garden or grocery store may be used if they are fresh and free from pesticides.

Some people like to add bananas, mangoes, papaya, or citrus fruits to the mix. Makes it taste much better, although in the early spring the body seems to crave these greens no matter what the taste.

©Copyright Butterfly Expressions, llc 2010   Butterfly Miracles with Herbal Remedies

COMBINATION INGREDIENTS   **COMMENTS AND COMPANIONS**

COMBINATION	INGREDIENTS	COMMENTS AND COMPANIONS
GUM formerly Gum & Mouth Relief	1.00 echinacea 1.00 white oak bark 0.50 goldenseal or oregon grape 0.25 propolis 0.25 prickly ash bark 0.50 cayenne	To be used as a mouthwash and is best used as a tea. Particularly effective for gum abscesses, bleeding gums, canker sores, mouth inflammations, sore throat, and subtle changes in the lining of the mouth after eating junk foods.
HD formerly Headache	1.00 wood betony 1.00 rosemary 1.00 peppermint	Pour 1 quart boiling water (distilled, filtered, or well water) over the herbs, cover until cool. Strain and sweeten to taste. I have never made this as a tincture, but I see no reason why it couldn't be. *Dosage is 3 tablespoonfuls every 2 hours, as needed. Not to exceed 5 or 6 doses in 24 hours.*
HGL to be used instead of LIC if licorice root is contra indicated	1.00 red clover 2.00 oregon grape 0.50 uva ursi 0.50 mullein leaf .25 cayenne 1.00 devil's claw 0.50 bilberry leaf 0.50 ginseng - panax	see notes for LIC Licorice root is contra indicated for use if a person has certain types of heart or cardio vascular problems. This formula, created without licorice root, can be safely and effectively used in these circumstances.
HP formerly Herpes Simplex	2.00 olive leaf 1.00 lavender flowers 0.25 oatstraw 0.50 hyssop 0.50 chamomile flowers 1.00 echinacea 0.50 slippery elm	Use for cold sores and other symptoms similar to the varieties of herpes virus. (From mono on through more serious problems.) Also has been useful in programs aimed at bringing relief to people suffering with shingles.

HVC	4 Tbl honey
	4 Tbl apple cider vinegar
	40 drops cayenne tincture
	     or 1 ½ tsp cayenne
	     powder
	water to make 1 qt
		Use cold for bleeding, insect bites, shock, blood clots, etc. Warm or cold for flu, increased energy, sore throats, circulation, etc. Drink ½ to 2 cups as needed, up to 1 qt or more a day.
		
		Warmth increases circulation—do not use hot or even warm when trying to stop a hemorrhage.

©**Copyright Butterfly Expressions, llc 2010**   **Butterfly Miracles with Herbal Remedies**

COMBINATION	INGREDIENTS	COMMENTS AND COMPANIONS

IB

formerly
Immune
Builder
or
Immune
Stimulant

2.00 marshmallow root
2.00 echinacea root
1.00 garlic
1.00 mullein leaf or flower
1.00 thyme
1.00 dong quai
1.00 rehamania root
1.50 elecampane

This one is usually made as a glycerite. Needs to be taken especially faithfully in the summer and fall months in preparation for the coming cold and flu season.

Dosage depends on age: Infants 1/4 teaspoon, children 1/2 teaspoon, and adults 1/2 to 1 teaspoon twice daily.

IBL

formerly
Iron/Blood

1.00 alfalfa leaves
1.00 comfrey root
1.00 marshmallow root
1.00 periwinkle leaves
1.00 red raspberry leaves
1.00 stinging nettle leaves
1.00 yellowdock root

Often improves the oxygen carrying capacity of the blood. These herbs are all found fresh in the inter-mountain area. *Dosage is 10 - 30 drops daily.*

Use for persistent anemia in pregnant women and everyone else. Use with wheat grass juice, broad spectrum enzymes, vitamin C, and folic acid.

IF

formerly
Infection
Fighter

3.00 echinacea root
2.00 oregon grape root
1.00 poke root
1.00 red clover blossoms
0.50 cayenne
0.50 yarrow leaf or flowers
1.00 usnea

This is an all purpose formula. Can be taken internally or as a tea for external compresses or wash. Use for any type of infection—infected injuries, sore throats, ear infections, and anything else that you can think of. Add usnea and yarrow or use the SS formula if strep or staph is suspected.

Goldenseal sometimes adversely affects estrogen and glucose levels. I use oregon grape in nearly all formulas, but goldenseal may be used if you prefer. Myrrh can also be substituted. See oregon grape on page 37 for further information.

KB

formerly
Kidney
Bladder

1.00 juniper berries
1.00 parsley root
1.00 dandelion root
1.00 uva ursi leave
0.50 buchu
0.50 lobelia
0.50 marshmallow root
0.50 oregon grape root
.250 astragalus
0.50 horsetail
0.50 cleavers
0.50 cornsilk
0.50 hydrangea

Can help cleanse and strengthen the urinary tract to accomplish the important job of eliminating toxins and wste products from the body. The kidneys also regulate the liquid to solids ratio in the blood and tissues. KB has no really effective bacterial fighters; best to use KB with IF (Infection Fighter) or RC (Red Clover).

10 - 20 drops every 3 to 4 hours, as needed.

Follow with milder KT (Kidney Toner) for a few weeks after a bout with infection.

©Copyright Butterfly Expressions, llc 2010   Butterfly Miracles with Herbal Remedies

COMBINATION	INGREDIENTS	COMMENTS AND COMPANIONS

KNA

formerly
Kelp
Nettles
Alfalfa

equal parts of
kelp
nettles
alfalfa

These three herbs contain all of the trace minerals, in adequate amounts and proportions, that have been identified as vital to good health. These herbs are particularly high in absorbable calcium, iron, iodine, vitamin C, and vitamin A. In addition, alfalfa contains a lot of a very usable form of protein.

KS

formerly
Kidney
Stone

1.00 stone root
1.00 gravel root
1.00 hydrangea
1.00 juniper berries
0.50 goldenrod
0.50 corn silk
0.50 stinging nettle

Use as an aid in dissolving kidney stones so that they may pass more easily.

Sipping lemon juice in water and then laying on your back with your butt and feet elevated can back stones out of the ducts and buy you some time to dissolve them!

KT
formerly
Kidney
Toner

1.00 marshmallow root
1.00 mullein leaf or flower
1.00 juniper

This is a mild and healing diuretic (without the side effects of drugs) and is one of my favorite formulas. The addition of .5 part of slippery elm makes it even nicer.

LB

formerly
Lower
Bowel

1.00 cascara sagrada
1.00 red clover
1.00 buckthorn
2.00 blue vervain
1.00 licorice root
0.50 uva ursi
0.50 bayberry
0.50 raspberry leaf
0 .25 lobelia
0.25 oregon grape root
0.25 ginger root
0.25 cayenne

This one is a bit stronger than CD (Colon/Digestive) and could be used alternately.   *Be mindful of the licorice and substitute bilberry, or just leave out the licorice if anyone taking it has a heart problem such as arrhythmia. Careful muscle testing should reveal whether or not licorice root is contra-indicated for a person.

LC

formerly
Liver
Cleanse

2.00 burdock root
1.50 fennel
1.00 yarrow leaf or flower
0.50 thyme
0.50 gotu kola
0.50 hawthorne berry
0.50 raw beet root
0.50 white birch leaves
0.50 dandelion root
0.50 red clover blossoms
0.50 plantain
0.50 oregon grape root
0.50 bilberry
0.50 devil's claw

Footzone balancing really helps when the liver is clogged or stressed. LC aids the liver in secreting necessary bile into the colon. When the liver is sluggish, the result is indigestion, constipation, ftigue, headaches, etc. It is recommended to strengthen the kidneys and colon while working with the liver but using either KB or KT for the kidneys, CD for the colon, and RC (Red Clover) to keep the blood clean of toxins and impurities.

Devil's claw and bilberry are specific to sugar problems associated with liver damage or clogging.
Others to add: oregon grape, wild yam, catnip, cramp bark, dandelion, skullcap, licorice.

©Copyright Butterfly Expressions, llc 2010   Butterfly Miracles with Herbal Remedies

COMBINATION INGREDIENTS

COMMENTS AND COMPANIONS

Lobelia/Cayenne   1.00 lobelia
1.00 cayenne

Use for speeding up slow labors. Alternate hourly with a tincture made with equal parts blue cohosh and dong quai during a labor that is progressing abnormally slowly or has stalled out a bit.

LCON

formerly
Lung
Congestion

3.00 fenugreek seed
3.00 pleurisy root
2.00 horseradish root
1.00 bee pollen
1.00 cayenne
1.00 hyssop
1.00 slippery elm bark
1.00 thyme
1.00 yerba santa
1.00 elecampane

This is a very hot tincture, due to the amounts of horseradish and cayenne used. If you are paying any kind of attention to health matters you should be catching things early and avoiding getting this desperate! But it sure works if you do get sick with one of the strong strains of virus and bacteria that we are seeing lately. I am glad to have something this effective in my repertoire!! Take 15-30 drops of tincture 3-4 times a day—more, if necessary.

For normal use, PL (pleurisy/lung) which is very effective but milder, is all that you need and deals with inflammation in the pleura at the same time.

LIC

formerly
Licorice
Combination

for adrenal and
pancreas
function and
stability

2.00 licorice root
1.00 goldenseal or
         oregon grape root
0.50 uva ursi
0.50 mullein leaves
.25 cayenne
1.00 devils claw
0.50 bilberry leaf
0.50 ginseng root

Formulated to strengthen adrenal and pancreas function to regulate blood sugar levels in both hypoglycemia and diabetes. Licorice is contra indicated for those with certain heart problems! Seriously!! Goldenseal can also create blood sugar regulation problems. If either is a factor for you, use the HGL formula instead.

Devil's claw and bilberry are specific to blood sugar related problems.

LN

formerly
Liniment
(can be made as
an oil)

*Be sure to label
the bottle as
"External use
only!!"
(because of the
arnica)*

2.00 comfrey root
2.00 arnica flowers
1.00 St. John's wort
1.00 lobelia
1.00 calendula flowers
1.00 angelica root
0.50 valerian root
0.50 ginger root
0.50 cayenne
essential oils
(pain & inflammation oils
such as birch, peppermint,
wintergreen)

I like to tincture this one in oil since it ***cannot be taken internally anyway (due to the arnica)***.

You can also make a salve that would be less runny. A salve is particularly effective.

These same herbs can be put together in dry pack form, then made into a strong tea and used as a soak or as a poultice. (Remember, if swelling is present, cool the decoction before placing on the area or soaking.)

©Copyright Butterfly Expressions, llc 2010   **Butterfly Miracles with Herbal Remedies**

COMBINATION   INGREDIENTS   COMMENTS AND COMPANIONS

LS

formerly
Labor
Stimulator

Make from previously made tinctures. Otherwise you will have a very large batch.

2.00 blue cohosh tinc
1.00 5-6 week formula tinc
0.50 bayberry tinc

Does not induce labor. If you attempt to use it in this way, you will most likely only make yourself even more uncomfortable for a time and then continue waiting anyway. Take advantage of the opportunity to learn patience (and waiting on the Lord's timetable).

Meant to stimulate a labor that is lagging or stalling out. Particularly effective if used as an enema.

LT

formerly
Lymph
Tonic

1.00 brigham tea
2.00 echinacea root
0.50 lobelia
1.00 oregon grape root
0.50 fenugreek seed
1.00 yucca

If brigham tea is unavailable, substitute .5 red clover blossoms, .25 chapparal, and .25 golden rod.

Use along with infection fighting tinctures in times of illness or whenever the lymphatic system seem to be clogged or needing assistance.

MC

formerly
Miscarriage
Aid

3.00 false unicorn
1.00 lobelia

In some women, a particular type of hormone imbalance slows or prevents the dissolving of the corpus luteum (a protective coating on the egg) so that the embryo can implant. This formula, taken at the first sign of spotting, can often correct this problem so the pregnancy can continue. If you have miscarried during the first 10 weeks of a pregnancy previously, consider taking MC as soon as you realize your are pregnant. *Serious hormone balancing work needs to be accomplished before the next attempted pregnancy!!* In the event of miscarriage anyway, this formula will help clean tissue and/or infection out of the uterus. Also give herbs and homeopathic remedies for excessive bleeding.

MH

formerly
Men's Herbs

3.00 marshmallow root
2.00 juniper berries
2.00 ginseng root
1.00 goldenseal root
0.50 cayenne
0.50 hawthorne berry

Aids in prostate, kidney, and bladder health and provides minerals needed to handle daily stress.

Use with ᴸᵉBalance and ᴸᵉEndo Relief essential oil blends. May need to supplement with zinc also

---

MIN

formerly
Minerals

3.00 alfalfa
2.00 nettles
1.00 red raspberry
2.00 oat straw
1.00 horsetail (shavegrass)
0.50 yarrow leaf or flower
0.50 kelp
0.25 chamomile flower
0.25 dill

General tonic, replenishing trace minerals. Excellent for use during pregnancy, while nursing and as a daily supplement.

Consider making as a glycerite or using as a tea for pregnancy and nursing.

©Copyright **Butterfly Expressions, llc 2010**   **Butterfly Miracles with Herbal Remedies**

COMBINATION INGREDIENTS

COMMENTS AND COMPANIONS

MP

formerly
Mastitis
Pack

0.50	cup of comfrey
0.50	cup of slippery elm
1.50	tsp goldenseal root
1.00	tbsp lobelia
0.33	cup mullein
0.33	cup poke root

Prepare in distilled water. Apply as a hot poultice to the affected breast area. Keep on for as much of the day and night as possible. Be sure to use LeEndo Relief essential oil blend on the feet and lymph areas of the neck and underarm. Take infection fighting herbs and kidney herbs such as the KT (Kidney Toner) formula. Hit it hard and stay on it until it is completely cleared.

MS

formerly
Multiple
Sclerosis

2.00	dong quai
2.00	ginkgo biloba
2.00	hawthorne
1.00	astragalus
0.50	St. John's wort
0.50	bee pollen
0.50	skullcap

Other things to consider supplementing:
KNA formula
Bilberry
Vitamin E
EPA oils
Selenium
Apis Melifica homeopathic
Multiple Organ & Glandular homeopathic
oats and oatbran

MULC

formerly
Mullein
Compound

1.00	blue vervain
0.50	chaparral
1.00	elecampane
0.50	brigham tea
1.00	ginseng root
1.00	hyssop
2.00	mullein leaf or flower
1.00	marshmallow root
1.00	oregon grape root
1.00	plantain
1.00	red clover blossoms

If brigham tea is unavailable, substitute .25 wood betony and .5 golden rod.

This is a good infection fighting formula and is especially suited to the respiratory system.

MW

formerly
Mature
Women's
Formula

6.00	dong quai
2.00	licorice root
1.00	wild yam
0.50	black cohosh
1.00	motherwort
1.00	St. John's wort
1.00	ginseng root, panax
0.50	passion flower

For women going through the menopause or experiencing symptoms of hormone imbalance such as hot flashes, night sweats, etc.

Use 20-40 drops 2-4 times a day as needed. Make sure mineral and vitamin intake is adequate by taking KNA. Add LeBalance and LeEndo Relief essential oil blends.

NAUS

formerly
Nausea

2.00	wild yam
1.00	peach tree leaves

Use 15-20 drops every 2 hours or as needed for nausea that is related to a certain type of hormonal imbalance. This formula is especially useful for pregnancy.

©Copyright Butterfly Expressions, llc 2010   **Butterfly Miracles with Herbal Remedies**

COMBINATION INGREDIENTS

COMMENTS AND COMPANIONS

NF
formerly
Nursing
Formula

2.00 blessed thistle
2.00 marshmallow root
2.00 red raspberry leaf
1.00 fennel seed

Increases the milk supply and the fats and proteins in the milk. If supply is ample but looks thin and the baby isn't gaining weight at the appropriate rate, use just the marshmallow root alone.

NS

formerly
Nerve
Special

1.00 black cohosh
1.00 hops
1.00 lady slipper - or sub
1.00 lobelia
1.00 skullcap
1.00 wild yam
(substitute 1 part each of motherwort and passion flower for the lady slipper which cannot be purchased at this time)

see notes—NV (Nervine) for further information

This formula can be mixed equal parts with St. John's wort for anxiety attacks, sleeplessness, etc. If you wish to make a formula with St. John's wort added, simply add .5 of a part of St. John's wort to the recipe listed here.

Occasionally someone will react poorly to a nervine type herb. For this reason there are 3 different formulas. It is possible to tincture each herb in this category separately and then build a tincture to suit each individual circumstance.

NT

formerly
Nerve
Tonic

useful for PMS
tension and
headache

2.00 oatsraw
1.00 skullcap
0.50 St. John's wort
0.50 lemon balm
0.50 lavender flower
0.50 rosemary
0.50 mother wort
0.50 passion flower

Nourishes and calms the nervous system. Use for anxiety, stress, premenstrual tension, hyperactivity, depression, nervous exhaustion, and recently acquired pain.

Consider adding KNA, BHM, or the MIN (mineral formula) to any nervine program, as well as appropriate essential oils.

NV

formerly
Nervine

1.00 spikenard
1.00 black cohosh
1.00 hops
1.00 lady slipper
1.00 lobelia
1.00 myrrh
1.00 skullcap
1.00 valerian root
1.00 wild yam
1.00 wood betony
0.50 cayenne
(can substitute 1 each motherwort and passion flower for lady slipper, with excellent results)

The strongest and most complete of the 3 nervine formulas listed here. Use to heal, calm, and strengthen the nerves. Nervine formulas make excellent pain relievers and are often useful in depression, ADHD, heart palpitations and irregular heartbeat.

Dosage is usually 15-30 drops every 3-4 hours, as needed.

Always consider adding minerals to the regimen—such as KNA, BHM or the MIN (Mineral formula). Also use essential oils as appropriate.

©Copyright Butterfly Expressions, llc 2010   Butterfly Miracles with Herbal Remedies

COMBINATION	INGREDIENTS	COMMENTS AND COMPANIONS

NVC

formerly
Nervine
Childrens

2.00 chamomile flowers
1.00 passion flower
1.00 catnip
0.50 peppermint

This is best made as a glycerite since it is intended to be used by children. Use 1/4 to 1/2 teaspoon 3 to 5 times a day; frequent small doses are more effective than larger doses. Can be given as often as every 15 minutes for a few doses. Is especially helpful with a colicy baby or one who startles awake during naps or at night. Helps stimulate the body's defenses as colds, flus, fevers, and other acute illness are getting started. Can be used as an alternate for CC (Children's Composition). The ingredients in this blend are more restful. Excellent used in the evening to promote restful sleep.

PARA

formerly
Parasites
(intestinal)

Recommended
that you try
Miracle II
neutralizer
and soap
instead. Much
gentler on the
intestines.
Call us or
google the
internet
for more
information.

2.00 burdock root
2.00 senna leaves
2.00 wormwood leaves
1.00 black walnut hulls
1.00 black walnut leaves
1.00 wintergreen leaves
0.50 fennel

0.50 tansy is used by
some people. I do not
use it—for some very
sound reasons!!

Can be made as a regular tincture, but for children I make it as a glycerite using 3 parts glycerine, 1 part honey, and 2 parts distilled water.

If made as an alcohol tincture use twenty drops; as a glycerite take 1/2 teaspoon. This should be done morning and night for 3 days. On the fourth day drink 1 cup of senna/peppermint tea. There is a divergence of opinion on how often to repeat. Version 1: wait 10 days and repeat. Version 2: repeat twice with a 3 day wait in between.

We have tried both methods and been successful at getting rid of parasites, but the effect on the colon was devastating. It took some months of acidophilus (acidophilus was also taken on the rest days between doses) and enzymes to rebuild the healthy flora and fauna of the colon. Also seemed to deplete vitamins and minerals from the body, so follow up with KNA or MIN or something.

The situation would have to be pretty desperate for me to try or recommend this to anyone anymore. I think that it is more harsh than is necessary for most situations!! We have had good success with gentler methods. Please see "Anthelmentic Herbs" on page 73 for recommendations that are gentler and more effective.

©Copyright Butterfly Expressions, llc 2010   Butterfly Miracles with Herbal Remedies

COMBINATION	INGREDIENTS	COMMENTS AND COMPANIONS

PF

formerly
Pancreas
Formula

1.00 devil's claw
1.00 bilberry leaf
1.00 sarsaparilla
0.50 ginseng root
1.00 mullein flowers &
     leaves

This formula contains herbals that are renowned for their blood purifying, diuretic, and toning properties. Their action involves most body systems and includes energizing and hormone balancing effects.

PL

formerly
Pleurisy
Lung

2.00 nettles
1.00 elecampane
1.00 usnea
1.00 comfrey root
1.00 blue vervain
2.00 pleurisy root
1.00 yerba santa
1.00 slippery elm
0.50 agrimony or yarrow
0.50 hyssop
0.50 cayenne

Be sure to use some essential oils that are appropriate for inflammation, respiratory congestion, and pain. ᴸᵉBreezey, ᴸᵉMariah, and ᴸᵉAspire work particularly well.

Dr. Christopher says to give a strong nettle tea and catnip enemas to really speed healing along.

PN

formerly
Pain

1.00 St. John's wort
1.00 valerian
1.00 wild lettuce
0.50 cayenne

May help raise the pain threshold by calming and quieting irritated nerve endings.

Use 20-30 drops every few hours, as needed.

Be aware that valerian is not suitable for everybody and should be used with particular caution with children. Indications of this situation would be that the person, instead of being calmed by valerian, would feel wired or nervous. Simply discontinue use and try something without valerian. See p 32.

For menstrual cramps, use VIB or CB formulas.

PPAC

formerly
Pain
Pack

recipe not in parts
1.50 mullein leaf or flower
3.00 slippery elm
1.00 lobelia
1.50 comfrey
0.50 oregon grape root
0.50 poke root
1.00 wormwood
0.50 ginger root

add for inflammation
1.00 bay
1.00 fenugreek seed

Works really well on sprains, bruises, etc. The sooner after the injury that you use it (before inflammation has really set in), the more effective it will be!

Use as a soak, a compress, or make as a liniment, oil, or as a salve. A compress seems to work the best because of the heat and moisture, but the other methods have the advantage of being much more convenient.

©**Copyright Butterfly Expressions, llc 2010** **Butterfly Miracles with Herbal Remedies**

COMBINATION   INGREDIENTS   **COMMENTS AND COMPANIONS**

PHB

formerly
Pregnancy
and
Hormone
Balance

(preparation for
pregnancy)

2.00 ginseng
2.00 sarsaparilla
1.00 black cohosh
1.00 licorice root
0.25 blessed thistle
0.25 false unicorn
0.50 squawvine
0.25 lobelia
1.00 chaste tree

This one is just as often needed between pregnancies as during a pregnancy. For lack of progesterone or inefficient adjustments of hormones during monthly cycle. *Absolutely necessary for women who have had repeated early first trimester miscarriages.* (See MC formula for further explanation.)

Use 15—20 drops 2-3 times a day as long as needed.

PT

formerly
Pregnancy
Tea
or
Tincture

2.00 plantain leaves
2.00 red raspberry leaves
1.00 alfalfa leaves
0.50 comfrey root or
         leaves
0.50 stinging nettle

The advantage to doing this one in a tea is that it assures that the mother is getting sufficient liquid to build blood volume and support the kidneys. Tea is inconvenient (so is pregnancy) and tastes nasty, but you will get used to it. Maybe you will even develop a taste for it. At any rate, you will know that you are doing the very best that you can for yourself and your baby. Use the tincture, if you must, as a back-up on days when you simply aren't getting the tea made.

Can help regulate hormones during pregnancy and make labor shorter and easier.

Drink 2 to 4 glasses of tea a day or use 25-30 drops each day if using in tincture form.

PRT

formerly
Prostate
Tonic

tonic,
infection
fighter,
and
anti-inflammatory

1.00 echinacea
1.00 yarrow
1.00 pipisseaw
         or horsetail
1.00 oregon grape root
1.00 sarsaparilla
1.00 hydrangea
0.50 ginseng root
0.50 astragalus
0.50 damiana
1.00 saw palmaetto
0.50 cornsilk or
         other kidney herbs

Inflammation, clogging, or infection of the prostate gland is indicated by frequent urination but with a decreased stream. Infection is often accompanied by pain, and/or chills, and fever.

©Copyright Butterfly Expressions, llc 2010   Butterfly Miracles with Herbal Remedies

COMBINATION INGREDIENTS

COMMENTS AND COMPANIONS

RC

formerly
Red Clover
Combination

*consider making
only 1/2 batch
makes a lot*

0.50	buckthorn bark
0.50	burdock root
0.50	cascara sagrada
0.50	chaparral
0.50	licorice root
1.00	oregon grape root
0.50	peach bark or leaves
0.50	poke root
0.50	prickly ash bark
1.50	red clover blossoms
0.50	sarsaparilla
0.50	stillingia root

Excellent blood and body cleanser. *RC is one of the most effective infection fighter formulas!!*

Use 20-30 drops 2-4 times a day. Can be used with CAC. RC is safe to use while pregnant or nursing, if necessary.

This has been used as a cancer formula when someone is pregnant or nursing. Be very faithful and keep the doses as high as can be tolerated by the body.
RC-L: add 1 part lomatium *(makes it very effective for bacterial or viral stomach flu).*

RH

formerly
Rosehips

fresh rosehips harvested in the late fall

apple cider vinegar
    (non distilled)
with alcohol

In the fall, gather ripe rosehips. Fill jar 1/3 full, blend in alcohol and apple cider vinegar (use equal parts of each).

Best source of vitamin C that I know of!

RM
formerly
Raspberry
Myrrh

equal parts of
raspberry leaves
and
myrrh gum

Use with CJ (Cascara Juniper) to strengthen the pancreas and stabilize blood sugar fluctuations.

SN

formerly
Sinus

4.00	brigham tea
2.00	ma huang
2.00	marshmallow root
2.00	burdock root
2.00	parsley root
1.00	yerba santa root
1.00	osha
1.00	eyebright or purple loosestrife
1.00	yerba mansa root
0.50	astragalus
0.50	cayenne
0.50	chapparal
1.00	oregon grape root
0.25	lobelia

substitute for red clover
under comments

Use for inflammation and infections of sinus cavities or for allergic sinusitis.

Use 12-20 drops every 3-4 hours to loosen and drain sinuses. Causes sinuses to drain but is not strong enough by itself for an intense viral or bacterial attack. Add one of the infection fighter combinations, APL (Anti-plague), RC, or pau d'arco and usnea at equal parts.
Also remember to use essential oils.

Ma huang is no longer available. Substitute 1.0 red clover blossoms, .5 chapparal and .5 golden rod for the Ma huang or add 2 more parts of brigham tea. If brigham tea is not available, add 2 parts of wood betony.

©Copyright Butterfly Expressions, llc 2010   Butterfly Miracles with Herbal Remedies

COMBINATION INGREDIENTS		COMMENTS AND COMPANIONS
SPRING	common cattail gumweed equal parts (volume, not weight)	An original blend that has proven extremely useful against some of the new potent strains of bacterial flus, particularly those affecting the lungs.
SS formerly Strep and Staph	2.00 usnea 2.00 pau d'arco 1.00 echinacea root 1.00 osha root 1.00 lomatium root 1.00 oregon grape root	Use for strep, staph, pneumonia, bronchitis, impetigo, pleurisy, sinusitis, tuberculosis and urinary tract infections. Usnea is an amazing staph and strep fighter! It grows here in our area, but sparsely, and is a pain to harvest. It likes the tops of very tall, dead or dying, pine trees!!
Super C formerly Super Cold and Lymph	1.00 echinacea 0.50 elder flower 0.50 lobelia 1.00 oregon grape root 2.00 red clover blossoms 0.50 white pine bark 0.50 cayenne	This is usually best done as a glycerite and is very effective for children. Excellent when taken at the onset of a cold or when in need of lymph draining for any reason. *Small doses—1/4 to 1/4 teaspoonful—taken more frequently is most effective*
TRT formerly Sore Throat Gargle	1.00 bayberry 1.00 goldenseal root 1.00 oregon grape (or myrrh) 1.00 echinacea root 0.25 cayenne	Dilute tincture with warm water (almost hot) and gargle. Removes phlegm, reduces pain, helps inflammation, and fights infection. There are essential oils that you can use which are much easier than this recipe.
TY formerly Thyroid	1.00 gotu kola 2.00 kelp 1.00 club or irish moss 1.00 parsley 2.00 oregon grape root 2.00 nettles 1.00 alfalfa	This recipe—or KNA—is effective in providing the minerals that are needed (and often missing in the mountain west) for healthy thyroid function. Thyroid medication has a lot of nasty side-effects and is not even meant to heal the thyroid. The medications are artificial thyroid hormones that send a signal to the thyroid gland that there is enough of the hormone in the body and it doesn't need to produce any more. The result is an ever increasing need for the medicines in ever increasing dosages until the side effects become quite nasty. Doctors play a game of moving people from one medication to another to keep the side effects manageable.

©**Copyright Butterfly Expressions, llc 2010   Butterfly Miracles with Herbal Remedies**

COMBINATION INGREDIENTS   **COMMENTS AND COMPANIONS**

VIB

2.00	cramp bark
1.00	blue cohosh
1.00	pulsatilla
1.00	motherwort
0.50	cloves

formerly
Vibrunalgia

Pulsatilla in herb form has not been available in my adult lifetime.   Consider a few doses of pulsatilla homeopathic in low potency in its place, if the indications are there.   I have never found an herb that is a good substitute for pulsatilla.

YU

equal parts of
yarrow
and
usnea

formerly
Yarrow
Usnea

This is a great bacterial, strep, and staph fighter.   Usnea is a lichen that grows in dying pine trees.   Has unique properties which are particularly effective against staph and strep strains and their mutations.   Also great for drying up any mucous over secretion situation and for lymph balance.

YW

2.00	goldenseal root
	or oregon grape root
1.00	blessed thistle
1.00	cramp bark
1.00	false unicorn
1.00	ginger root
1.00	red raspberry leaves
1.00	squawvine
1.00	uva ursi
1/8	cayenne

formerly
Young
Women's
Formula

Helps women in their childbearing years who have infertility or trouble with lack of estrogen.   Will often, if taken for a month or two, straighten out irregular periods, heavy clotting, profuse flow, etc.
Also helpful with kidney, liver, and bladder problems in women and essential during prolapsed uterus situations.

Consider Sepia homeopathic in addition.

WC

3.00	wild cherry bark
	process separately -
	w/o heat and add later
2.00	white pine bark
1.00	elderberries
1.00	spikenard or mullein
1.00	elecampane or
	fenugreek
1.00	licorice root
1.00	coltsfoot
1.00	horehound
1.00	slippery elm bark
1.00	lobelia

formerly
Wild Cherry
Cough Syrup

WC is an excellent cough and expectorant formula.   It is best to give it in small doses frequently—1/2 to 1 teaspoon, depending on age.   WC will liquefy mucous in the throat, lungs, and sinuses, quiet a cough if that is what is needed, and relieve the heat and dryness of sore throats.

WC should be taken with other appropriate infection fighting herbal formulas.

This is a glycerite tincture.   Make up 60 ounces of menstrum using a ratio of 60/40.   This breaks down to 5 1/4 cups glycerine and 2 1/4 cups distilled water.   Reserve 10 oz of the water glycerine mixture for tincturing the wild cherry bark.   The wild cherry bark must be done separately because it cannot be heated. Let the wild cherry portion sit for 24 hours and then add it to the rest of the recipe after the cooked part has cooled.   Place everything ***except the wild cherry bark*** (herbs and glycerine/water mixture) in a glass jar with a tight lid.   Process in a cold pack canner with the water gently boiling, as you would for cold pack canning fruit, for 2 hours.   Cool completely.   Strain both herb batch and wild cherry batch and combine.   I like to add 4 drops of benzoin essential oil as a preservative at this point.

©**Copyright Butterfly Expressions, llc 2010   Butterfly Miracles with Herbal Remedies**

BBL

The herbs in this tincture combine to make an outstanding antispasmodic, nervine, and pain reliever. BBL will bring relief to anything that manifests with spasms or a pulsing sensation. Examples might be coughing, muscle spasms, and abdominal cramping—whether menstrual or digestive in nature. Very effective when used for toothache, earache, certain types of stomach pain, headaches, and smashed fingers or toes. Also excellent for the pain of boils, broken bones, pleurisy, etc. BBL is the first thing I reach for whenever I hurt.

BBL is more than a pain reliever. It also helps to rebuild nerves in damaged areas of the body and brain, and has a special affinity for the spine and the motor nerves at the base of the skull. A dropperful taken at bedtime or added to the tub for a relaxing bath is the best way that I know to promote a good night's sleep. BBL can be given internally, or in the case of broken bones, smashed fingers, or similar ills, can be applied topically or used as a soak or poultice.

A few drops of BBL, along with mullein or garlic oil, or well-diluted ᴸᵉDeliverance (1 drop diluted with 1/2 teaspoon almond or olive oil), is good in the ear for an earache. The BBL acts as a pain reliever while carrying the medicinal properties of the oil deeper and more rapidly into the canal and increasing the antibacterial effects of the oils.

A couple of dropperfuls of BBL in a tub of warm water relieves cramping—from muscle cramps through menstrual ones. Used as a liniment on the abdomen or any muscle that is cramping brings almost instant relief.

Consider BBL for convulsions in children and babies and as a treatment for asthma, both during the attack and as part of a long term program.

Caution: Because of the lobelia in this blend (which is a large part of why it works so well!!) if BBL is needed for long term pain relief, it is advised to administer a mild stimulant such as peppermint tea or a few drops of cayenne tincture, especially for small children. The best way to determine if this is necessary is to monitor the pulse rate and administer the stimulant if it slows too much. In sick children and adults the pulse is usually accelerated, making the slowing of the pulse a part of the healing properties and a very good thing. The need for a stimulant is very rare and certainly no reason to not use this amazing healer.

You might want to consider having more than one of these available since its uses are so many and so varied. Also many people prefer one that is glycerine based for use with infants and small children.

©**Copyright Butterfly Expressions, llc 2010   Butterfly Miracles with Herbal Remedies**

©Copyright Butterfly Expressions, llc 2010   Butterfly Miracles with Herbal Remedies

Chapter Twenty Three
Making Herbal Salves

Herbal salves are wonderful things! They are convenient to use and very powerful. The recipes that follow are made from herbals with some essential oils added; excellent salves can be made using just essential oils without the plant material.

Basic Salve Ingredients: (Salve ingredients are broken down and explained further on the next page)
    Carrier-type oil
    Herbals, fresh or dried (or tinctured)
    Solidifier
Optional Ingredients:
    Essential oils
    Lighteners
    Preservatives

Use a 1:10 ratio, approximately, of herbs to oil; add more oil if the salve seems dry as it is cooking.
For each cup of oil used, you will need approximately 1.4 ounces of beewsax.
1 tablespoon vitamin E oil, 3 drops benzoin essential oil, 1 easpoonp benzoin tincture, or ½ teaspoon benzoin herb powder
    may be added as a preservative.

Place the herbs in the oil. Heat in crock pot or oven allowing the mixture to get no hotter than 180° F. Once the mixture has reached 180° allow it to cook for 2-3 hours. The herbs will have begun to look a bit grey and be a little bit crispy. The mixture should be stirred a few times as it cooks. If you use fresh herbs, you will have to cook the mixture longer. Fresh herbs have a lot of moisture in the leaves and stems. This moisture must cook completely out or your salve will mold. When the salve is hot, little bubbles will form on the surface and then pop. This is the moisture evaporating off. Keep cooking the salve until there are no more bubbles and the herbs are grey and slightly crispy as described above.

During the last hour of the cooking process, begin melting the beeswax. I use old bread pans that I bought at a thrift store. You will not be able to use the pans for anything else after the beeswax has been melted in them (unless you are willing to work very hard at getting them clean again). You must watch the beeswax closely as it heats. Overheated beeswax goes dark and smells terrible.

When the herbs are finished cooking, strain them just as you do for other tinctures. Press out as much of the oil as you can. Place the oil back into the oven to keep warm. When the beeswax is melted and the oil and the beeswax are approximately the same temperature, stir them together. The oil should be just a little bit warmer than the wax. If the oil is too cold the wax will resolidify as you pour it in. This makes little lumps in your salve that will not stir out. The only solution to this problem is to reheat the entire batch, whipping and stirring it frequently as it reheats. This is not fun, so watch your temperatures carefully.

On occasion, you may not have an ingredient that you need in dry herb form, or you want to make a salve more quickly. You may use tinctures to make salves instead of fresh or dry herbs. Using only tinctures, instead of dry herbs, makes a light colored and very pretty salve. The salve will be pale tan/green instead of dark herbal/plant green.

©**Copyright Butterfly Expressions, llc 2010   Butterfly Miracles with Herbal Remedies**

A salve made with just tinctures will not be as potent as one made from dry bulk herbs, but it will be much quicker and easier to make. This strength is probably fine for lotions or face creams. If you are trying to heal a burn or draw out a serious infection, you should make your salve from herbals—fresh ones if possible   Most herbal salves that you buy commercially are made with tinctures.

If you are adding any tinctures to your salve, do it now while the salve is hot so that the alcohol and water will evaporate away. Wait until the bubbles are finished dissipating. The bubbles are water and this moisture can cause your salve to mold if not completely evaporated out. You will need at least 3 dropperfuls of tincture for each part called for. This is a lot of liquid. You may have to reheat the salve a little to get rid of all the moisture.

When the moisture has been removed, let the salve cool. The cooling process is where the real work begins. For the first hour or so the salve must be stirred frequently—every 5 minutes. The top of the salve cools more quickly than the rest. A crust forms on the tops which will become lumps if not thoroughly stirred in. Attention paid here will give you a beautiful smooth salve; be careless or sloppy here and you will have a lumpy salve) or you can spend a lot of time with a hand mixer trying to get the lumps out).

When the salve is cool add vitamin E/wheatgerm oil or any essential oils that you wish to use. Essential oils are fragile, so be sure that the salve is cool before adding them. The other ingredients of the salve are carrier oils. Carrier oil breaks down the therapeutic properties of essential oils over time, making the oils in the salve less effective. Essential oils for therapeutic purposes should be added to a small amount of the salve at the time of use instead of while making the batch of salve. Any essential oil added now, however, will act as a preservative for the salve. You will be able to keep it unrefrigerated for longer periods of time without the salve getting rancid.

If you are in need of a really strong drawing or healing salve, use as much fresh plant material as possible. You must let the salve cook until every bit of moisture has cooked out of the plants and out of the salve. This can take up to 12 hours. A salve made with fresh herbs such as comfrey, mullein, plantain, and marshmallow is amazing.

Since herbs are at peak medicinal quality at different times of the year, I often make an oil tincture from each herb when it is at its peak medicinally. At the end of the season (late fall) the oils can be combined to make a salve, following the basic instructions above.

Salve making is not as hard as these two pages of instructions make it sound. Mostly it is just time consuming and messy. It also feels very rewarding to have made something so wonderfully medicinal for your family and friends.

©Copyright Butterfly Expressions, llc 2010   Butterfly Miracles with Herbal Remedies

General Information about Salve Making Ingredients
Oils:

Almond oil, by itself or in combination with other cold pressed oils such as grapeseed and safflower, is excellent. Almond oil has very little odor, is readily available, and has a low rancidity factor.

Olive oil is a fairly good choice for salves. It can make the consistency of a batch of salve a little unstable, however. A batch that is just the right thickness in the fridge becomes runny on a hot day and difficult to use. No amount of beeswax solves this problem. Olive oil has a low rancidity factor and is good for the skin. It has a slight aroma unique to itself, which you will not notice in a salve using herbs anyway (an herbal salve has its own unique aroma—slight but still there). For light lotions and lip salves, you probably want to use almond or grapeseed oil.

Grapeseed oil is an excellent medium; it is especially nice when blended with almond oil. Grapeseed oil has a low rancidity factor, and is reasonable in price.

Flaxseed oil is an excellent choice because it is emollient. making it excellent for skin problems. Flaxseed goes rancid easily; store any salve made with it in the fridge. It is also quite expensive.

Safflower and Sunflower oils are often rancid when you buy them, or become rancid quickly.

Lard is sometimes suggested as a base. Some sources claim that lard carries toxins and impurities into the body. Dr. Christopher used lard almost exclusively for his salves. your lard was rendered by you from a pig you raised without chemicals and drugs, it will be safe for salve making. Salves made with lard go rancid very rapidly and must be stored in the fridge. This is enough to make me choose something else. I have used lard when I had nothing else available, even on broken skin, and had no infections or other problems.

Sesame oil should be cold pressed (never use the toasted variety). This oil goes rancid quite quickly at room temperatures, but when not rancid, is very emollient to the skin.

Wheat germ oil Don't use as the base oil—very high rancidity factor. You simply won't believe the smell if wheat germ oil goes rancid! A tablespoon of wheat germ oil added to the salve at the end of processing as describes on the previous page adds wonderful healing properties to the salve. Wheat germ oil is high in vitamin E and antioxidants.

Coconut oil does not make a good base for a salve. However, I love to rub it on my skin, adding essential oils as I go. Coconut oil absorbs slowly, but makes the skin feel so smooth and moist.

Solidifiers:

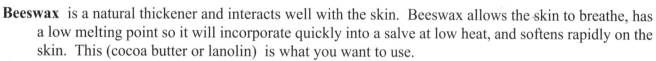

Beeswax is a natural thickener and interacts well with the skin. Beeswax allows the skin to breathe, has a low melting point so it will incorporate quickly into a salve at low heat, and softens rapidly on the skin. This (cocoa butter or lanolin) is what you want to use.

Cocoa Butter has a lower melting point than beeswax. It may be used alone or with beeswax. Cocoa butter is usually quite expensive, but it gives a salve a very nice creamy texture.

Paraffin is a petroleum product and not absorbable by the skin. In other words, ***not recommended*** for salve making.

Lanolin—anhydrous—is the closest lubricant to what is produced by our sebaceous glands. It is readily absorbed into the skin, and helps the skin retain moisture. (Hydrous—not the recommended anhydrous—lanolin is 10% lanolin and 90% water. It is expensive. Why pay big bucks for water? Hydrous lanolin has a wonderful consistency if using straight on the skin, but has too much water to use as a salve base. Anhydrous lanolin is hard to find and bit difficult to use. Beeswax is best.

Other Optional Ingredients:

Glycerine Use only vegetable glycerine. Beat into the finished salve as a lightener or sweetening agent (very nice in lip balms). Glycerine has many healing properties.

Aloe Vera Gel makes the salve very light and easy to apply. Aloe vera has many healing properties. It is especially nice added to burn salves. Use caution. Allergies to aloe vera are quite common.

©**Copyright Butterfly Expressions, llc 2010   Butterfly Miracles with Herbal Remedies**

BHM
(Formerly Total Body)

This is an adaptation of a Dr. Christopher recipe. It is a very effective, all-purpose salve. Use to aid healing in sprains, breaks, strains, skin rashes, and minor burns.

6.00	comfrey root
3.00	mullein leaves or flowers
0.75	marshmallow root
1.50	white oak bark
0.25	wormwood
1.00	lobelia (can use slightly less)
0.75	skullcap
0.75	black walnut leaves
0.75	heal all or plantain
1.25	red clover blossoms
0.75	oregon grape root

BHM-Plus
(Formerly Drawing Salve)

This salve has all the same herbs as the BHM salve, with the addition of herbs that are specific to infections and suppurating sores. This is a very potent salve! It is better at drawing out infections than anything I have ever seen on the market—both herbal and otherwise.

3.00	comfrey root
2.00	mullein leaves or flowers
0.50	marshmallow root
0.75	white oak bark
1.00	wormwood
0.50	lobelia
0.50	skullcap
1.00	black walnut leaves or hulls
1.00	plantain (or heal all)
0.75	red clover blossoms
0.50	oregon grape root
0.50	bay leaf
0.50	fenugreek seed
0.25	uva ursi
0.75	chapparal
0.50	poke root
0.50	wormwood

CM
(formerly Skin Irritation)

A basic salve for healing non-open wounds such as breaks and sprains and for any rash or skin irritation. Layer with arnica oil if there is swelling. Consider using the BHM salve discussed above.

1.00	calendula flowers
1.00	marshmallow root
1.00	comfrey root
0.50	mullein leaves or flowers

PPAC
Pain Pack Oil or Salve

This recipe is also in the tincture file. PPAC is effective when there as been severe bruising and blunt instrument trauma. It is best used with Butterfly Express, llc. essential oil blends ᴸᵉDeeper or ᴸᵉPaine.

1.50	mullein leaves or flowers
3.00	slippery elm
1.00	lobelia
1.50	comfrey root
0.50	oregon grape, goldenseal, or myrrh
0.50	poke root
0.50	wormwood

add the following if inflammation is present
1.00	bayleaf or arnica
	(arnica only if the skin in unbroken; use the homeopathic for otherwise)
1.00	fenugreek seed

LN
(Liniment)

Ingredient list on page 23 of this document.

©Copyright Butterfly Expressions, llc 2010   Butterfly Miracles with Herbal Remedies

Miracle Salve
(Formerly Healing/Burn)

This is an amazing healer—even for very severe burns. This salve was originally made for one of my sons. He had 3rd degree burns from ankle to hip. No antibiotics or nonherbal anti-infectious agents of any kind were used.   We soaked his leg in cold water with lots of lavender oil for the first 24 hours and gave him garlic capsules, IF, and RC tinctures by mouth.

This salve was later used on my husband's very severe burns. It was estimated that 65% of his upper body was 3rd degree burns; another 10% had 2nd degree burns. These burns included his face, ears, and hands and were so severe that it was several months of hard work before he could raise his chin to look you in the eye. The muscles of the shoulders, arms, hands, back, and abdomen were also severely damaged. (We got to watch muscle tissue regrow and srtiate properly. Not a pretty sight, but fascinating.)

This salve was renamed Miracle Salve at this time because we know that it really does work miracles. We saw, and have continued to see, miracles with its use!

Once again, as with our son, no antibiotics or nonherbal anti-infectious agents were used. My husband did not see a doctor or go to a medical facility through this experience. The external burns were not the scary part. He had gasped as the explosion happened and inhaled flame and noxious gases. But that is another story for another day.

Most of his skin healed beautifully. One hand, used to remove his burning clothing, suffered some major muscle damage. This hand is still a bit unsightly but it usable and pretty strong. He has no fingerprints on either hand, and he lost some dexterity in his fingers.

The shape of his nose, ears, and lips was permanently changed a little bit, but you would have had to know him well before the burns to notice. There are two very small scars on is face and a couple of other small ones on his body. He looks wonderful!

Ingredients for Miracle Salve:

3.0	comfrey root	2.0	lobelia
2.0	plantain		(use less if pain is not a factor)
2.0	mullein	2.0	oregon grape

The amounts above requires 13 1/2 cups of almond oil. You might consider using some jojoba or apricot oil because of their emollient properties.

For a single batch, 1 lb of beeswax is about right. This amount is approximate because there is a lot of difference between the consistency of solid beeswax and the beeswax that comes processed into little pellets and is light in color. This measurement is for the solid block variety of beeswax. You would probably need quite a bit more if you were using the pellets. If you use too much and your salve is a bit solid, just stir in a little additional almond oil.

When the salve has cooled (after the wax has been added), add 2 cups of vitamin E oil. Vitamin E speeds healing, rebuilds damaged cells, and reduces scarring. I generally use wheatgerm oil. Since I am going to add essential oils, shelf life and rancidity will not be a factor.

©**Copyright Butterfly Expressions, llc 2010   Butterfly Miracles with Herbal Remedies**

For a single batch of the above recipe I added the following essential oils:

5 ounces lavender	2 ounces helichrysum
2 ounces tea tree or eucalyptus	2 ounces geranium

Do not use more essential oils in a batch than is shown above. This is a lot of essential oil, but we were dealing with a major burn. Infection was a concern—we didn't see any except a tiny bit along the ridge of one ear where it was difficult to keep the salve. Essential oils can be a bit caustic, especially to already damaged skin. You can always add more essential oils later if you feel like you need it.

The addition of 1 cup of glycerine and 1 cup of aloe vera gel will make a salve lighter and more easily spread. The aloe vera is cooling and soothing to skin. Both aloe vera and glycerine have many fine healing properties of their own.

When using salve on deep burns, consider spreading the salve on **non-stick** gauze and then placing the salve covered gauze on the burn. You should prepare all of your pads first and then move the patient into position for the dressing change. This will make the dressing changes shorter and less painful for the burn victim.

The addition of essential oils to your salves <u>will</u> prevent infection! We have dealt with some horrendous burns using this salve, essential oils, and herbal tinctures and we had never dealt with infection. Be sure to add infection fighting herbs to the diet or medicinal regimen.

Fluids are very important. Because of my husband's internal burns, he was unable to take any fluids for several days. This made these burns very scary. Push the fluids from the very beginning and things will go much better.

©**Copyright Butterfly Expressions, llc 2010   Butterfly Miracles with Herbal Remedies**

Practical Uses

(Any essential oils mentioned in this booklet are manufactured and sold by Butterfly Express, llc. I created most of these blends, so I know and love them. You may, of course, substitute other essential oils of your choice. Any tincture formulas mentioned are also my own or common recipes known and used in the herbal world for many years. The recipes are supplied in this book in section 2.

The suggestions come from years of practical application. They are certainly not everything there is to be said about any ailment. If you have some things you have tried that are effective, please share them with me if you would care to. There is so much we all can learn from each other.)

Ailment	Suggestions
Abscess, dental	As soon as the abscess begins to form, take RC or other infection fighting herbs. I prefer RC because it is a blood cleanser. White oak bark mixed with water to make a paste and applied to the area acts as a drawing poultice. White oak bark tastes nasty but it is the strongest thing I know of for gum problems and gum health in general. Rinsing the mouth frequently with essential oils such as ^{Le}Deliverance may work just as well or even better.
Acne *Hormones sometimes play a part in acne. If hormones are involved use YW for young ladies and MH for young men.*	When the colon and kidneys are not working properly, the body uses the skin as an eliminative organ. Anything that the body cannot utilize or does not want is sent out of the body through the skin. No amount of creams, soaps, or even clear water will keep the skin clean enough to clear the acne. You must start with the colon, the kidneys, and the blood. Diuretic and alterative herbs are often helpful. Some of these are: buchu, cleavers, corn silk, dandelion, echinacea, horsetail, parsley, and yellow dock. Suggested combinations: RC for cleansing the blood, CD for getting the bowels going, and KT or KB to support the kidneys. Drink plenty of water and eliminate as much processed food, unhealthy fats, and sugar from your diet. Eat lots of fresh fruits and vegetables.
Aging	The Korean Ginseng Research Institute has published study results in which ginseng showed impressive results in lengthening the life span of cells in laboratory cultures. Ginseng also stimulated cell growth when adequate nutrition was present but inhibited cell growth under adverse conditions. These studies were conducted on a variety of cell types including skin, liver, lymph, and nerve cells. Rosemary is a powerful antioxidant. Use to rejuvenate the body and slow the aging process. (See DHEA discussion in memory section of this chapter.)

©**Copyright Butterfly Expressions, llc 2010   Butterfly Miracles with Herbal Remedies**

Ailment	Suggestions
Anti-inflammatory	bilberries, black cohosh, butcher's broom, brigham tea (gastrointestinal), chaparral, fenugreek (gastrointestinal and skin), marshmallow, mullein, plantain, pleurisy root, sarsaparilla, slippery elm, white wild yam, willow bark, Combinations: AP-joints; LN, PN, PPAC-muscles and tendons; CD-colon; PRT-prostate; LCON, BRON, PL-lung, bronchials, pleura; RC-blood.
Arthritis	All alterative herbs (chapter 13), angelica, bilberries, blue cohosh, cayenne, sarsaparilla, wild yam, yellow dock Herbal combinations AP and RC. AP, besides being taken internally, can be made into a liniment, salve, or compress. Essential oils can bring a great deal of relief.
Asthma	bee pollen for the B vitamins; Combinations: BRON, KNA, LT, MIN, PL, WC; a tea made with brigham tea, licorice, and lobelia is sometimes helpful. Essential oils on the chest and feet should also be used.
Athlete's foot	Athlete's foot is a fungal infection. Long ago we used to soak infected feet in a tea made from the RC recipe with extra black walnut hulls added. Now we soak feet using Butterfly Express, llc LeDeliverance oil. I am sure many other essential oil blends would also work very well. Soaking the feet in oil and water carries the oil deeper than just putting it on straight. Be sure to take infection fighter and blood cleaner tinctures such as IF and RC. Soak the feet at least once a day for a week. Continue to take the tinctures for a few weeks.
Bleeding	The treatment, of course, depends on why and from where the blood is coming. If you have cut yourself, powdered cayenne works very well. Just apply it to the wound, cover with a piece of cloth or tissue and be patient for a few minutes. Fresh yarrow leaves or yarrow essential oil applied to the wound will also stop the bleeding. Cayenne by mouth at the same time would also be helpful. For menstrual or postpartum bleeding use cayenne, shepherd's purse, yarrow, or mistletoe. Chlorphyll and the homeopathic tissue salt combination known as bioplasma also work incredibly well.
Blood sugar	oregon grape and bilberries seem to stabilize blood sugar. Tonic herbs on a regular basis, exercise, and nutritious foods are a must.
Breasts, fibrocystic	To balance estrogen levels use chaste tree or false unicorn; kelp or KNA to improve thyroid function; dandelion and yellow dock for liver health and, most important of all is angelica. Take it by mouth and, if possible, rub angelica oil on the breasts. Supplements of live acidophilus cultures will help maintain bowel function

©Copyright Butterfly Expressions, llc 2010   Butterfly Miracles with Herbal Remedies

Ailment	Suggestions
Bronchitis	There are two recipes in this booklet specific to lungs and the bronchii. They are BRON and PL. SS and RC have been effective against some of the new "super bugs" that we have seen in recent years. Yarrow can be added to help dry out the lungs. Lobelia is one of nature's very best expectorants. Expectorants dissolve mucous, making it easier for the body to cope with. The herbal combination BBL (which has lobelia in it) will either soothe the cough, if that is what is needed, or cause the body to clear the lungs by expectorating the mucous. Coltsfoot, elder berries, and elecampane are also good herbs for the lungs.
Bruises	The very best thing I know of for bruises is arnica, in oil or homeopathic form. Arnica should not be placed on open wounds; the homeopathic form is used here. PPAC as a poultice will pull out pain and stiffness. Chaparral, witch hazel, and yarrow are also recommended, although arnica and the PPAC (and some good essential oils) are all that my family has ever needed.
Burns	Miralce Salve on page 117 is all that you will need. As soon as possible, after the burn has taken place, apply cold water and lavender essential oil. Tonic and nervine herbs can be of great assistance. Use RC or IF to prevent infection.
Candida	Candida albicans bacteria is a naturally occurring part of the intestinal tract. The candida, or yeast, infection that creates so many health problems in an overgrowth of candida in relation to the other helpful bacteria in the digestive system. A diet that is too acidic, a hormone imbalance, low thyroid, diabetes, a weakness in the immune system caused by poor diet or an unhealthy lifestyle, stress, oral contraceptives, or a regimen of antibiotic therapy are among the reasons for this problem. Changes in diet and lifestyle, essential oils, and the CAN formula used consistently, usually get things back under control.
Capillary fragility	Clinical trials have shown that bilberries strengthen capillaries throughout the body. This has been demonstrated in studies conducted on such various body systems as the eye and the kidneys. Bilberries also build collagen.
Cardiac (see heart)	A list of heart tonic herbs is provided on page 34

©Copyright Butterfly Expressions, llc 2010   Butterfly Miracles with Herbal Remedies

Ailment	Suggestions
Cholesterol, high	Ginger has been shown to lower cholesterol levels in the blood and in the liver by increasing its excretion and impairing its absorption. The allicin in garlic also lowers cholesterol levels. Because the aroma of garlic is offensive to some, manufacturers have produced "odorless" garlic products. These products have concentrated levels of allicin. Allicin is converted in the body to allicin. Clinical trials of these products indicate that they are just as effective as garlic. An "odorless" garlic supplement should supply at least 10 milligrams of allicin. Garlic should also be added to food for people with high cholesterol levels, heart disease, hypertension, diabetes, candida, asthma, respiratory tract infections, and gastrointestinal problems.
Chronic fatigue	Chronic Fatigue Syndrome has become so widespread in the United States as to qualify as a rising epidemic. We have had quite a lot of experience with the effects of this syndrome, but the solution is too complicated for this section of this booklet. Please visit the "Useful Information" section at www.butterflyexpressions.org for an article about possible homeopathic, herbal, and nutritional help for this syndrome. Herbal combination CF specifically targets this syndrome.
Colds	The most important thing to know about colds is that a strong immune system will help you have less of them to deal with. If you do get a cold, diaphoretics to help you "sweat it out" are the first things to reach for. Elder flower, peppermint, and yarrow are helpful for the feverish feeling. Plantain slows the secretion of mucous membranes in the nose and throat but acts as an expectorant in the lungs. Because of this dual (and almost contradictory) action, plantain alleviates cold symptoms and prevents the cold from dropping into the chest.
Cold sores	Many cold sores are caused by the virus, herpes simplex. (See herpes section.) This virus nests in the nerves endings along the jaw in many adults. The virus can be activated by a rise in skin temperature, by a fever, or even just being in the sun. Other triggers for the virus might include poor diet, dietary triggers such as chocolate, stress, hormone imbalances, and a poor immune response. Strengthen the immune with nourishing herbs and fight the virus with essential oils because they have viral fighting properties.
Colic	Herbs for colic include: catnip, chamomile, dill, fennel, hops, and lemon balm. Tincture formula recipes found in this booklet that are helpful for colic in babies and/or adults are: COL, COLA, and the catnip/chamomile combination. Catnip/chamomile is my favorite for infants and small children.

©Copyright Butterfly Expressions, llc 2010   Butterfly Miracles with Herbal Remedies

Ailment	Suggestions
Conjunctivitis (eye infection)	(Sometimes referred to as pinkeye) The EB formula is the one that I have relied on for years. An alternative remedy is 2 parts echinacea, 2 parts eyebright herb, and 1 part calendula flowers. Make a weak tea, strain very well, and put the liquid in the eyes. Always treat both eyes, whether or not they are both infected at the time.
Constipation	Constipation can be caused or aggravated by lack of fiber in the diet, not drinking enough water, lack of exercise, and neglecting or ignoring signals from the bowels that a bathroom break is needed. Stool softening agents include: sweet almond or olive oil, apples, apricots, asparagus, black walnut, buckthorne, cascara sagrada, chamomile, chickweed, chicory, fig, flaxseed, prune, red raspberry, safflower, and slippery elm. Adding fiber to the diet is also helpful. My husband, who had severe colon problems as a younger man, uses wheat and oat bran combined with coconut and molasses as a breakfast cereal. It opens the bowel, gently, every time. Be sure to drink plenty of fluids with whatever program you follow.
Convalescence	The convalescent stage of any serious illness is very important. Serious illnesses can sometimes leave problems that, in homeopathy, are called "never the same since the . . . .". Fatigue, body aches, migraine headaches, poor circulation, etc., become chronic illnesses. Attention should be paid to digestion and the assimilation of nutrients at this time. Circulation is another important thing to get reestablished in the body. Extra rest and a more gradual return to normal routine is the best preventative. Nourishing herbs include: gentian, echinacea, dong quai, comfrey, and the high mineral tea recipe on page 79. Chlorophyll, bee pollen, vitamin C, probiotics and the tonic herbs listed in chapter 5 are often helpful.
Coughs	Which herbs you use to treat a cough with herbs depends entirely on what you want to accomplish. Usually, you want to encourage the cough to bring up and rid the body of mucous. Expectorant herbs do this. Elder flower is one of the best because it acts as a sedative and pain reliever but will liquefy muscous and expel it if that is needed. Mullein is often used with mustard in a poultice on the chest to break up mucous. Elecampane and licorice are excellent expectorants; they are usually used in a formula with other herbs. Lobelia is used to calm persistent, dry or nervous coughs. Lobelia will also expectorate mucous if that is what is needed. Mullein tea is another good way to calm a lingering cough. ***Of course, my personal favorite is the WC combination. It combines many herbs and applies to most situation, whether expectoration or calming is needed.*** WC is mild enough for children, but strong enough to be effective for adults.

©Copyright Butterfly Expressions, llc 2010   Butterfly Miracles with Herbal Remedies

Ailment	Suggestions
Depression	Sometimes depression is a nutritional deficiency. Nerves are just not getting the vitamins and minerals that they need. Tonic and nervine herbs and herbal combinations can often bring a lot of relief. NS, MT, NV, NVC, and BBL in this booklet are recommended. Essential oils should be an integral part of the program, also. Some herbs noted for depression are: black cohosh, catnip, chamomile, chaste tree, damiana, ginseng, hops, kelp, lobelia, motherwort, oatstraw, passion flower, skullcap, St. John's wort, valerian, vervain, wood betony, and tonic herbs according to nutritional need. B vitamins should also be emphasized.
Diabetes	Diabetes is a serious disease which can sometimes be controlled, at least in the early stages, by close attention to diet and herbal nutrition. Herbs that are considered by experienced practitioners to be helpful are: bilberries, garlic, gentian, licorice, wild oats, and wood betony. I have had very good success in the early stages of pancreatic problems and early diabetes with two simple herbal duos. The first is equal parts of cascara sagrada and juniper. These two herbs support the colon and the kidneys. The second combination is equal parts of raspberry leaves and myrrh. This formula targets the endocrine system and the pancreas in particular. The essential oil, dill, stabilizes blood sugar rapidly and ^{Le}Endo Relief can be used to gradually strengthen the entire endocrine system. *Ginseng* should be part of any program for endocrine system improvement. Ginseng is an amazing herb in the treatment of diabetes, hypoglycemia, and any kind of fatigue.
Diarrhea	Occasional diarrhea is the body's way of removing toxins from the body and re-establishing balance; it is not something to be concerned about. Chronic diarrhea, on the other hand, can deplete the body's supply of fluid and minerals, especially potassium, in a very short time. Chamomile, fennel, ginger, lavender, lemon balm, licorice, plantain, pleurisy root, red raspberry, or slippery elm teas can be nourishing and soothing. Any of the digestive tonics listed on page 34 should be considered on an individual basis.
Digestive problems	Most herbalists believe that basic digestive problems can be avoided by attention to lifestyle, diet, and stress factors. Page 34 of the tonics chapter lists many digestive tonics. It should be noted that digestive tonics come in several varieties—stimulants, relaxants, bitters, and tonics. Some herbs act in more than one capacity. Dandelion, gentian, fenugreek, and turmeric are noted stimulants. Chamomile and catnip are good relaxants. Peppermint, depending on quantity, can stimulate the digestive process and relax a nervous stomach at the same time. Herbs such as agrimony angelica, dandelion elecampane, fennel, stone root, and uva ursi are considered bitter herbs. (In some reference books, all digestive herbs are listed as bitters.)

©**Copyright Butterfly Expressions, llc 2010   Butterfly Miracles with Herbal Remedies**

Ailment	Suggestions
Dizziness/Vertigo	Dizziness and vertigo are not the same thing, but they both have many causes and the causes of each are often the same. Some of these causes include lack of circulation to the head or inner ear, low blood pressure, ear infections, heart problems, nerve and nervous disorders, and allergies. The herbal response in each cause will be different from that of the other causes. Some basic suggestions are: gingko biloba and cayenne for vertigo and dizziness related to circulation to the head. The B vitamins, particularly B-6, are essential to normal functioning of the brain.
Ear infections	Many, many years ago a new doctor in town thanked me (in jest) for helping to feed his family with my 3 (at that time) children's ear infection appointments. It made me so mad I set out to find a better solution—and I did. I began poking holes in garlic oil capsules and putting a couple of drops in my children's ears on a regular basis. If they had a current infection and were hurting, I would add a couple of drops of BBL. Never again did we go to the doctor for anything ear related—or anything else unless it was broken or very badly torn. The EO recipe in this book is also a good way to treat ear infections. Remember the BBL. BBL handles pain and dissipates inflammation. If the ear does rupture, it will do so in little pin-pricks that heal rapidly with no damage to the ear drum! This has been documented and is amazing! ***Warning! Garlic essential oil is too strong for putting in ears! It would burn and damage badly!*** 1 drop of garlic oil in 5 ml of almond oil—mix well—would be a workable blend for ears.
Endometriosis	Patches of endometrial tissue growing where they should not be respond to menstrual hormones in the same way that the endometrial lining of the uterus responds, growing and then bleeding. Because the blood is not able to escape the body in the normal way of menstruation, it forms painful congestion in the abdomen and then forms scars and adhesions. There are many possible causes for endometriosis; the only common link that I see is the over production of estrogen. Hormone balancing herbs for this condition include: black cohosh, blue cohosh, calendula, chamomile, chaste tree, cinnamon bark dandelion, false unicorn, goldenseal, motherwort, white oak bark, red raspberry leaf, pulsatilla, rosemary, saw palmetto, skullcap, vervain, wild oats, wild yam, and witch hazel. These herbs cover three predominant types—nervines and pelvic relaxants, astringents for congestion and heavy bleeding, and hormone balancers.

©Copyright Butterfly Expressions, llc 2010   Butterfly Miracles with Herbal Remedies

Ailment	Suggestions
Fatigue	Ginseng's notable effects on fatigue and stress are discussed on page 60 of this booklet. Ginseng lives up to its reputation in every particular. Herbal combinations for various types of fatigue include AD, BHM, EW, HGL or LIC, HVC, IBL, MH, MIN, and KNA (kelp, nettles, alfalfa). Cayenne is always a good addition when energy and stamina are needed.
Fever	CC (children's compound) is my favorite first response to illness and fever in children. This combination combines diaphoretic herbs with gentle infection fighters. FV is also a good combination. Both formulas should probably be used with IF, RC, SS, or FN, depending on what type of bug you are fighting.
Fibroids	Fibroids are non cancerous growths either in or on the walls of the uterus. Fibroids are believed to be associated with high estrogen levels. Since estrogen stores in fat cells, fibroids are more common among women who are over weight. I believe that fibroids are also associated with thyroid dysfunction. Fibroids are painful and difficult to treat, but we have had a great deal of success both in "bleeding them off" and preventing their reoccurrence. Prevention, of course, includes herbs that balance hormones and herbs that support the thyroid (see the hormone balance and thyroid sections in this table. Yarrow (tea, tincture, and essential oil) is the key. Yarrow is very astringent and caused the uterine lining to tighten, forcing the fibroid to disconnect. This can create enough bleeding to be a scarey experience. You must be prepared with herbs such as cayenne, mistletoe, and shepherd's purse. I would also have homeopathic bioplasma and liquid chlorophyll on hand. We successfully bled off a fibroid—carefully and slowly—during a pregnancy (doctors recommended abortion!). I believe the fibroid was connected to both hormone and thyroid insufficiencies. The baby was born prematurely with a very small placenta, but survived and is a darling and healthy little boy (my grandson, by the way. Can't even imagine life without him! His mother, while proof reading this section, added a smiley face and "Me, too" to this section.)
Flatulence	Flatulence and gas are indications of digestive disturbances. Digestive tonics are listed on page 34. Carminative is the term used by herbalists for herbs that eliminate or expel gas from the stomach or intestines. These herbs are listed in chapter seventeen. The herbal combinations (in the recipe section) for relief of these conditions are COL, COLA, and catnip/chamomile.

©Copyright Butterfly Expressions, llc 2010   Butterfly Miracles with Herbal Remedies

Ailment	Suggestions
Flu	The various flu varieties are viral in nature. The management of flu should include essential oils (essential oils can kill viruses) and homeopathics. Herbs can be very helpful in relieving lung congestion, coping with fever, alleviating body aches, and stimulating the immune response. (Butterfly Express, llc, sells a very interesting flu kit that covers all of these modalities. Information about the uses of the various components is provided at www.butterflyexpressions.org).
Food poisoning	I'm not sure that food poisoning can be treated with herbal remedies alone. I have had good success with either homeopathic Arsenicum album or Carbo vegetablis. Herbs are essential in the follow up stage to rebuild the digestive system. Digestive tonic herbs are listed on page 34. Probiotics, acidophilus, chlorophyll, and papaya are also helpful in the rebuilding stage. Rebuilding thoroughly and consistently can prevent a lifetime of problems.
Gallstones	The formation of gallstones indicates that digestive problems are causing calcium to be absorbed improperly. The absorption problem probably applies to other minerals, as well, and is causing other unrecognized problems throughout the body. Digestive tonics (page 34) are helpful. The GI formula, taken before each meal, can alleviate symptoms and gradually dissolve small stones. An improvement in diet and exercise is an absolute necessity. I passed gallstones 3 painful times as a younger woman. Then I cleaned up my digestive tract and my diet and have not endured that pain for the last 15 years.
Gas	(see flatulence)
Gout	Gout is the accumulation of uric acid crystals in tissues. While you may first feel the gout in your toes, uric acid crystals are also being deposited in joints, tendons, kidneys, and other tissues. Gout is considered a form of arthritis. I agree, but also consider all arthritis to have a very strong uric acid component. Dietary factors are known to contribute to both bout and arthritis. A diet high in red meats, yeast, fats, refined carbohydrates, sugars, and too many calories contribute to gout. On the other hand, too little protein and too little fat consumption also create gout. Alterative/adaptogenic herbs are helpful as supplements to the diet. Diuretic herbs (chapter 7) remove the uric acid from the tissues. I often have people go into their yards or gardens, harvest some mallow to drink as a tea for a few days. This solution is very convenient, very inexpensive, and always impresses them about herbs as a solution as opposed to expensive doctor's visits and drug therapies.

©Copyright Butterfly Expressions, llc 2010   Butterfly Miracles with Herbal Remedies

Ailment	Suggestions
Gum/Mouth problems	The very best *herbal* remedy I know of for gum and mouth problems is white oak bark. Make a tea and rinse the mouth frequently. There are many essential oils that balance bacteria in the mouth and are beneficial as mouth washes.
Headache	Headaches have a multitude of causes; I have rarely seen a headache sufferer who had only one type of headaches. Headaches can be hormone related, impaired circulation to head and brain, associated with allergic or chemical reactions, stress or lack of sleep induced, or misalignment in the neck, back, or tailbone. The first step is to assume lack of circulation and take cayenne with ginkgo biloba. If there are any other signs of hormone imbalance, begin an immediate regimen with hormone balancing herbs. Structural misalignment is best treated with ᴸᵉMillenia essential oil, cranial/sacral treatments, and visits to a chiropractor. Many times the nervine formulas NS, NT, NV, NVC, and BBL will relax the muscle, alleviate tension, and aid sleeping. Keep a record or foods eaten and substances exposed toso that when a headache comes on you can track potential causes. Muscle testing can be a big help with this.
Heart problems	Heart tonics are listed on page 34. Cayenne, hawthorne, and yucca have been very effective for myself and others in the past. Attention to exercise, starting very slowly with cardiovascular exercises and being consistent is very helpful. Eliminate stimulants such as caffeine and excess chocolate from your diet. ᴸᵉVitality essential oil should be used on the chest several times a day.
Hemorrhoids	Hemorrhoids are varicose veins in the lining of the rectum. Sometimes they are visible; just as often there are some up inside that you cannot see. Hemorrhoids result in rectal bleeding and pain during bowel movements. Lack of exercise and insufficient fiber in the diet contribute to hemorrhoids. Anything that you do to improve vein health will improve hemorrhoids. Possible herbs to try are angelica, butcher's broom, cayenne, dandelion, hawthorne, mistletoe (for a short period of time), saw palmetto, yarrow, and yellow dock. Essential oil blends ᴸᵉCypernium, ᴸᵉVitality, and ᴸᵉVisibility, applied topically, have proven helpful for many people.
Hepatitis	There are many forms of hepatitis, all of which are very serious. Medical attention should be requested. Herbs that might also aid in the recovery process include the liver tonics listed on page 34. Dandelion and milk thistle in combination may be particularly effective.

©**Copyright Butterfly Expressions, llc 2010   Butterfly Miracles with Herbal Remedies**

Ailment	Suggestions
Herpes simplex	Herpes is a common viral disease that produces cold sores around the mouth and/or blisters around the genital area. The HP combination was created to combat herpes simples. HP was created in conjunction with ^{Le}Simplicity essential oil to root the virus out of its bases along the nerves. (Please see the cold sore section.) The amino acid L-Lysine is often helpful. Taking L-Arginine may trigger an outbreak, but the outbreak will be related to the rooting out of the virus in the nerve bundles and is actually an opportunity to erradicate them with viral fighting essential oils. Lemon balm and the essential oil distilled from the same plant, Melissa, are used with success for herpes.
Hormone balance	Hormones play a big role in so much of our lives and it is a fallacy to believe that only women have hormones that go out of whack! In my experience, so much of what presents in men as temper, anxiety, mid life crisis, depression, and moodiness has its roots in hormones. The most important thing you can do for your hormones is make sure your diet includes the basic vitamins and minerals, that you get some exercise every day, and that you expose yourself to sunlight whenever you can. Hormonal tonic herbs are listed on page 34. Herbal combinations that are helpful are YW for young women and women of child bearing age, MW for women approaching or in their menopausal years, and MH for men and teen age boys. KNA or TY are also helpful. I know I keep saying this in so many categories, but essential oils can be very helpful with hormones.
Hypertension	Many of us have been taught that salt is a contributing factor in high blood pressure. Nothing could be further from the truth. A poor quality, highly refined salt whose chemical nature has been changed by processing is a problem all around. But a good quality, natural, preferably a sea salt, provides many trace minerals that are often missing in our diets. This kind of salt actually helps to stabilize blood pressure. I have seen this many, many times, especially as a midwife with pregnant clients. Please eliminate normal salt and increase the amount of mineral rich salt that is consumed if you fight high blood pressure. BP is an herbal formula that has proven useful with hypertension for many years. Being a natural remedy, it brings the body into balance; it is just as effective for low blood pressure as for high blood pressure. The herbs in the heart tonic list on page 34 should also prove useful. Once again, exercise, diet, and stress management are absolutely essential. Mistletoe has an immediate effect in lowering very high blood pressure. It is not the entire answer. Other herbs and changes in diet need to be employed at the same time. Never take mistletoe for an extended period of time (more that a few weeks, at the very most).

©Copyright Butterfly Expressions, llc 2010   Butterfly Miracles with Herbal Remedies

Ailment	Suggestions
Immune support	Immune tonics are listed on page 34. Of this list, garlic, ginseng, and elethero are the fastest acting. Bee pollen, ginger, goldenseal, and licorice seem to rebuild by nourishing gradually throughout the entire system. Nearly all of us could benefit by some attention to strengthening our immune systems. (See lympathics section.)
Indigestion	Typically the pH range of the stomach is 1.5 to 2.5. The use of antacids typically raises that level to 3.5 by neutralizing hydrochloric acid. Hydrochloric acid is the primary digestive acid of the stomach and is not the culprit in indigestion. This destruction of hydrochloric acid and increase in pH relieves the symptoms of acidity and indigestion, but it inhibits the action of pepsin. Pepsin is a necessary enzyme in the digestion of protein. In other words, while you feel better, you are actually damaging your digestion. If you have chronic indigestion it would be better to focus on aiding digestion than to focus on blocking digestion with the use of antacids. Although much is said and written about hyperacidity and stomach acid, it is far more common for indigestion to be the result of deficient gastric acid secretion than the other way around. It was once believed that ulcers were caused by acidity. We now know that peptic ulcer disease is caused, to a great extent, by an overgrowth of the bacteria *Helicobacter pylori,* which cannot exist in a properly balanced digestive system. I think it is worth the time and space here to give you a list of diseases associated in recent research with low gastric acidity. Some of these are: addison's disease, asthma, autoimmune disorders, celiac disease, dermatitis, diabetes, eczema, gallbladder disease, hepatitis, chronic hives, lupus, osteoporosis, pernicious anemia, psoriasis, rheumatoid arthritis, rosacea, thyrotoxicosis, and hyper and hypothyroidism. Studies have shown that the ability to secrete gastric juices decreases with age. With a lifetime of proper attention to diet and the use of digestive tonic herbs, I don't believe this has to be. The best digestive herbs are listed on page 34. In previous generations, and still in much of Europe, every meal is preceded by a "bitter" dish. This bitter is to stimulate the digestion and notify it that a meal is to follow. This is an excellent idea. It can be easily accomplished herbally by taking a few drops of GI tincture or other herbal bitters before every meal.
Infection	Infection can apply to infection in a local area such as a cut or it can be used to describe a systemic attack by a viral, fungal, or bacterial agent. In any case, the herbs that fight infection are much the same. Take internally as many and as much of them as you can tolerate and the situation calls for. If it is a local infection, apply the herbs as a poultice or soak the area in a strong tea. A list of single herbs that are considered anti-infectious does not really tell the story. A good herbal combination that includes blood purifiers, liver herbs, and support for the kidneys is the only effective way to fight infections. Examples of these are APL, BAC, FN, HP, IF, RC, Super C, YU. Others such as BRON, EUST, PL, SN and SPRING target very specific body systems or bacteria. First response remedies include CC and COMP.

©Copyright Butterfly Expressions, llc 2010   Butterfly Miracles with Herbal Remedies

Ailment	Suggestions
Infertility	Infertility is one of the most difficult situations to assist with. Watching a couple ride the monthly roller coaster is hard on everybody. We have been successful many times, however, and those words, "Guess what? I'm pregnant" are some of the most beautiful in any language. Every situation is so unique that general advice such as this is only the first few steps. The first place to start is with a Zone Balance (sometimes called Foot Zone). This therapy can remove blocks wherever they might exist and give an overview of the problem from a perspective different that the medical one. Next, balance hormones until they are running perfectly—in both husband and wife. Third, investigate what herbs and foods contain which vitamins and minerals and make sure you are getting everything that your bodies need. Avoid soda and caffeine and get some exercise—not to excess, but a little every day. Herbs that might help (you will be healthier for using them) are the hormone tonics and general tonics listed on page 34. Good luck and God bless you!
Insomnia	Most of the nerve tonic herbs (page 34) and nervine recipes (pg 105-6) can be used as sleeping aids from time to time. Include in your evening routine some relaxing and unwinding time such as a bath in essential oils or reading something uplifting and calming. Try adding relaxing essential oils to your bath. (Watching something violent on TV does not count!) Tinctures can be useful, but I find a cup of relaxing tea to be far more likely to be effective. *Celestial Seasonings* Sleepytime tea, or something similar, (found in most grocery stores) is easy and quite pleasant tasting. I find essential oils diffused in my bedroom at night to be most pleasant and helpful.
Joint problems	(see arthritis section)
Kidney stones	Besides indicating a problem in the urinary tract, kidney stones (like gallstones) indicate a problem with digestion. (Please see section on gallstones). The pain from kidney stones comes from the stones trying to pass through the ducts. Sipping lemon juice, cold and fresh is best, constricts the ducts and forces the stones up and out. Lying on your back with a pillow under your hips and your feet up in a chair (your knees should be bent) at the same time brings almost instant relief. You may have to repeat this procedure for a long as necessary several times a day until the stones are ready to pass. Take as much of the KS formula as you can every day. Eventually, the stones will be smaller with fewer rough edges. How long? As long as your patience with lying on the floor a couple of times a day holds out. It really depends on how many and how big the stones were. After about 2 weeks add the KT formula whenever you take the KS. The stones will pass, not painlessly but endurably. If there are many of them, this make take more than one time. When the stones are gone, continue taking the KT formula and concentrate on your digestive system so that you never have to do this again. I passed kidney stones twice a year for several years before I did some cleansing and rebuilding programs. I haven't had a kidney stone (or gallstone) for many years now. Feels great!

©Copyright Butterfly Expressions, llc 2010   Butterfly Miracles with Herbal Remedies

Ailment	Suggestions
Laryngitis	A strong tea using marshmallow, thyme, or white pine bark is helpful. I like to add a lot of honey and some lemon juice and sip on it all day.
Laxative	I hate the word laxative so badly that I hesitated even to put it here, but constipation is such a common problem that something needs to be said. That something is that constipation usually responds very well to an increase in fiber and fluids and consistent mild exercise (at least 20 minutes a day). Oat bran consumed raw, or in good quality whole grain cereals, is best. Commercial fiber formulas can also be helpful, but avoid any that contain senna. Add lots of fruits and vegetables to your diet—include prunes for the first little while— and drink plenty of fluids. If you have been using stimulant laxatives, even herbal ones, you will have to teach your colon better ways of functioning. You can do this by following the above regimen and being sure to sit on the toilet at the same time every day (even when there is no urge). I would recommend doing this a few minutes after each meal and after exercising. This is an important step. Begin weaning yourself off of the laxatives. For the first week, take a stimulant laxative such as cascara sagrada or senna. Use the least possible dose necessary to reliably create a bowel movement in the morning. Each week decrease the laxative dose by half. Pay close attention to diet, fluids, and exercise. If constipation returns, go back to the previous weeks dose and pay even better attention to diet, fluids, and exercise. Decrease the dosage, of course, if diarrhea occurs. If your colon is damaged by diverticula or coated with the accumulation of years, you may experience some cramping or nausea. It will not last and may be necessary. Once your bowels are moving regularly—once a day is nice, but more often is certainly better— maintain colon health by (you guessed it) attention to diet, fluids, and exercise. Fruits, vegetables, and fluids are the keys to colon health.
Liver problems	The best solution I know of for fixing and avoiding liver problems is to do a cleanse similar to the one described in chapter 18. I try to do this for 3 or 4 weeks in January (after the junk of Halloween, Thanksgiving, and Christmas) and then again in the Spring. In the Spring I sometimes just make green drinks—a lot—and drink them faithfully. There is a suggested recipe for green drink on page 99.

©Copyright Butterfly Expressions, llc 2010   Butterfly Miracles with Herbal Remedies

Ailment	Suggestions
Lymphathcs	The lymphatic vessels drain waste products from the tissues, and in most of the body, run parallel to the arteries and veins. The lymph vessels carry the lymph fluid to the lymph nodes where they are filtered. The thymus is the major regulatory gland of this system. To a very great extent, the health of the thymus determines the health of the entire immune system and the efficiency of the lymph system. The thymus, proportionally, is very large in infants and children. It actually shrinks as the body grows, becoming a relatively small gland by adulthood—at least in the United States and other industrialized nations. Why is this? Anything that compromises the immune system compromises the thymus. The lymphatic system has no pumping mechanism. There is no organ, like the heart is for the circulation, that moves lymph along. Exercise is essential for lymph drainage. Suggested herbs are: bayberry, burdock, calendula, cleavers, dandelion root, echinacea, goldenseal, licorice, myrrh, nettles, oregon grape, plantain, pleurisy root, poke root, red clover, and red root. Wormwood is recommended on some lists for really serious conditions. Wormwood should be used with great caution and and as a small percentage in formulas with other herbs taking the lead.
Macular degeneration	Macular degeneration is the leading cause of serious visual loss in the United States. A diet rich in fruits and vegetables is associated with a lowered risk for macular degeneration. Antioxidant formulas and gingko biloba have been shown in clinical trial to halt, and even reverse, macular degeneration. Consider vitamin E when looking for antioxidants. Bilberries are excellent combined with gingko biloba. High blood pressure increases the risk for and the progress of macular degeneration as does hardening of the arteries. Lets take care of our health to take care of our vision!
Menopause	My favorite herbal handbook takes 14 pages to talk about menopause. Don't want to do that here. As hormones change during these years, many other changes in the body can be triggered. Women, use the MW formula (or something similar) regularly. Men (yes, men have hormone changes in their lives too), the MH formula is excellent. Everyone, nourish yourselves with the general tonics (page 34), consider nervine herbs as needed, learn to use and enjoy essential oils. I am well into or past menopause and loving it. I am healthier, happier, more productive, and more energetic than I have ever been. I plant to get younger every year, literally, for many years to come!

©Copyright Butterfly Expressions, llc 2010   Butterfly Miracles with Herbal Remedies

Ailment	Suggestions
Memory problems	DHEA (dehydroepiandrosterone) is the most abundnt hormone in the bloodstream. It is found in very high concentrations in the brain, with levels declining dramatically with aging. Recent studies show promising results for DHEA as a balancer of the hormones that regulate many of the body's activities. Declining DHEA levels have been linked in clinical studies to such conditions as diabetes, obesity, high chloesterol levels, heart disease, arthritis, memory loss, and a host of age related conditions. Gingko biloba also shows promise in clinical trials and studies for the improvement of memory and mental capacity. Ginseng and gota kola also show promise as memory enhancing herbs.
Miscarriage	Miscarriages are far more common than is generally supposed. Clinical estimates are that 1 in 2 very early pregnancies miscarry, appearing to be only a delayed or extra heavy period. It is also estimated that 1 in 6 women who have a positive pregnancy test later miscarry. It is also estimated that with proper care and the use of natural remedies, over half of threatened miscarriages can be successfully brought to full term with a healthy baby. This is a very amazing statistic. Even when the miscarriage completes, the herbal remedies make the subsequent bleeding and cramping much less severe, and recovery time is shortened remarkably. MC and CB formulas are used when miscarriage threatens. Should the miscarriage occur in spite of all efforts, follow-up treatment is important. LeMillenia applied across the abdomen helps the uterus return to a prepregnant state more quickly than would otherwise occur. LeMillenia also helps a woman find courage and a hopeful vision of the future. Herbs for bleeding following a miscarriage include cayenne, shepherd's purse, mistletoe, and bioplasma homeopathic
Motion sickness	Ginger tea, or ginger tea with a little bit of cayenne, taken before traveling is often helpful. leEZ Traveler essential oil and homeopathic Arsenicum album taken in low potency are also recommended.
Muscles/muscle relaxant	AP (in recipe section) is an anti-inflammatory. BHM (also in recipe section) is the best all around herbal combination for muscles. It should be taken internally and applied as a poultice or a salve at the same time. LN (liniment) is very good applied externally. If there is bruising, arnica oil should be applied. Any of the nervine herbs make good analgesics, but the BBL formula is my favorite antispasmodic and analgesic. I have been using this one for many years. BBL is discussed further on page 113.
Nausea	Some herbs for nausea are: alfalfa, chamomile, clove, dill, fennel, ginger, hops, lemon balm, licorice, peach leaves, peppermint, and spearmint. If nausea persists day after day, the cause should be looked for. Digestive imbalance creating ulcers, etc., or an allergic reaction, among other things, should be investigated.
Nerves/nervous system	Chapter 11, which beins on page 55, is a discussion of nervine herbs.

©Copyright Butterfly Expressions, llc 2010   Butterfly Miracles with Herbal Remedies

Ailment	Suggestions
Ovarian cysts	Ovarian cysts are the result of imbalanced hormones and a toxic system. Any solution must include improvement of the diet, eliminating tea, coffee, sodas, as much junk food and refined flour and sugar products as possible. Exercise is also a must. Drink plenty of fluids and use diuretic herbs to flush toxins from the tissues. Black cohosh, blue cohosh, chaste tree, and false unicorn should be used to balance the hormones. Pulsatilla, which has not been available except in homeopathic form in my life time, is essential. Dandelion, plantain, horsetail, and/or yarrow will act as astringents in dissolving and passing the cysts and in generally cleansing the system.
Pain	Chapter 11 discusses nervine, antispasmodic, and pain relieving herbs. Remember, pain is a friend in that it signals us that something is wrong in the body or mind and needs attention. Never just dull the pain without attempting to find and fix the underlying causes.
PMS (Premenstrual Syndrome)	A father of several young women, when asked by his young son what the initials PMS stood for replied, "Pretty Mean Stuff". Symptoms of PMS include headache, general aches and pains and backache, constipation or diarrhea, nausea and vomiting, hypoglycemia, tension, mood swings, panic attacks, and food cravings. These things do not need to be the norm for women. YW tincture and wild yam cream used faithfully have brought relief to many women. For other hormone balancing oils, see the hormones section of this chapter. LeWoman Wise and BBL tincture on the abdomen and back often bring amazing relief during the period itself. Careful attention to diet and exercise all month long can also make a difference. Be patient with the hormone balancing herbs. They are nutrition, not magic. Use them consistently and give them a little time to act.
Parasites	Parasite herbs, and alternative programs, are discussed in chapter 17. False unicorn is mildly anti-thelmenic and does not destroy the normal bacteria cultures of the bowel. It balances hormones at the same time.
Pregnancy	Covering all the aspects and possible complications of pregnancy from an herbal standpoint would take an entire, large book. They have already been written and are available to you. I have been a midwife for 25 years and the most important advise that I can give you is to eat well! Cover all the nutritional needs of the body and do it all the time. Avoid as much convenience and junk food as you can. Whole grains, real fruits and vegetables, and protein on a regular basis. Drink plenty of water and red raspberry leaf tea. Get the trace minerals that you need by using MIN or KNA. Supplement with a good, natural prenatal vitamin—make sure it has a natural iron (not made-made) and folic acid. Folic acid is found in green leafy vegetables and broccoli. Blackstrap molasses is an excellent source of iron. Iron needs vitamin C to absorb—use rosehips or some other none ascorbic acid source. Ascorbate acid is the kind your body can process. Finally, don't forget the FSW formula the last 5 or 6 weeks of the pregnancy. This herbal tonic make a world of difference to both Mom and baby during labor and delivery.

©**Copyright Butterfly Expressions, llc 2010   Butterfly Miracles with Herbal Remedies**

Ailment	Suggestions
Prostate problems	Prostate enlargement seems to happen to most men, especially as they grow older. Frequent urination, decreased stream, and eventually, incontinence are the leading symptoms. Prostate problems should be dealt with at this stage; don't wait for pain, chills, and fever indicating an infection to treat herbally. If herbal remedies do not bring a quick response, a medical exam to rule out more serious problems should be sought. The MH formula taken from time to time throughout the years will prevent a multitude of problems. The PRT formula is specific to clearing inflammation, clogging, and infection. I would add RC if chills and fever indicate an infection. The statistics on saw palmetto for prostate—both for prevention of and for the treatment of existing problems—are amazing. Please see page 38 for one interesting study. Buchu, because of its action on the kidneys and bladder makes an excellent companion to saw palmetto.
Psoriasis	Psoriasis can be the result of an extreme allergic reaction to something—laundry product, etc. It is more likely the result of either impaired uptake of vitamins and minerals as the result of low gastric acidity or other digestive problems. Digestive herbs are listed on page 34. These herbs, or the GI tincture taken before meals will eventually change this and the psoriasis eventually clears. This is not an over night thing, but the effects on overall health is amazing. Another case of psoriasis is endotoxins circulating in the blood stream from a toxic colon. Sarsaparilla is the answer here. (Please see page 63 for further explanation of this situation). As with digestive disturbance, clearing toxins from the bloodstream takes a bit of time and effects every body system. Be sure to support the kidneys and colon with KT and CD during this process. Skin problems are often the most difficult of ailments to treat, and they can be very stubborn to clear up. Applying topical creams is much like applying a band-aid to to a deep and infected wound. So many times, the skin problem is occurring because the skin is being used as an eliminative organ. This only occurs when the kidneys and colon are too unhealthy to do their jobs properly. The kidneys and colon must be the first priority. When they are functioning, the skin will begin to clear. This is often true even when the skin problem has an allergy component.
Radiation	Ginseng has been shown in some very interesting studies to protect cells during radiation therapies and to facilitate the rebuilding of cells when the treatment is finished. Wormwood also has a reputation for protecting the body from radiation, but it is a much harsher herb.
Respiratory system	Respiratory herbal formula recipes included in this book are: BRON, LCON, MULC, and PL. These formulas should **always** be used in conjunction with infection fighting formulas such as APL, BAC, IF, RC, SS, or YU. Other respiratory herbs are angelica, aniseed, bee pollen, coltsfoot, elecampane, garlic, horehound, and mullein.

©Copyright Butterfly Expressions, llc 2010   Butterfly Miracles with Herbal Remedies

Ailment	Suggestions
Sinus	There are two excellent recipes in this booklet—SN and EUST. They should be taken with one of the infection fighter formulas mentioned in the paragraph above on the respiratory system. I would use EUST if there is mucous draining down the back of the throat and SN for every other type of sinus congestion or problem.
Skin	(See Psoriasis in this section)
Sore Throat	The TRT formula makes an excellent gargle for sore throat. Super C can also be useful. Fight back, immediately and consistently, with one of the infection fighting herbs listed in the Respiratory System section of this chapter. Applying essential oils topically can bring a lot of relief and help beat the "bug".
Stress	Coping with stress is a learned behavior. One couple I know attended a stress management class after the husband had suffered a stroke. He was busily taking notes about the amazing things he was learning; his wife was sitting there bored to death and thinking, "Doesn't everybody do this?" However, with that said, the fact is that it is almost impossible to manage stress if the nerve endings are not getting the nutrition that they need and you are not getting sufficient sleep. Formulas for feeding nerves include NS, NT, NV, and for children NVC. These are not narcotic formulas; they nourish and heal the nerves. Nevertheless, they bring almost instant relief from nervous tension and can help you sleep more soundly.
Sunburn	Aloe vera is the most respected herbal remedy for sunburn. St. John's wort, applied topically as a tea, is also excellent. St. John's wort can be purchased as an essential oil or as a carrier oil—the essential oil can be added to almond or olive oil to create a carrier oil. The very best treatment for bad sunburns is the Miracle Salve, page 119.
Thyroid	A malfunctioning thyroid is often the result of missing nutrients. These nutrients may be missing in the body because they are not being absorbed or because they are not present in the diet. KNA and TY tincture formulas will provide the missing nutrients. Look to digestive herbs to change the absorption patterns.
Urinary tract infections	UTI's should be treated with KB and infection fighting herbs. My personal favorite is RC with IF a close second. After the infection seems to have cleared, I like to follow up with a few weeks of KT taken at least twice a day. This removes the last of the congestion and returns the water levels of the cells throughout the body to normal. (Stressed kidneys always lead to stressed cells everywhere.)

©Copyright Butterfly Expressions, llc 2010　　Butterfly Miracles with Herbal Remedies

Ailment	Suggestions
Vaginal infections	(See the section on Candida; the same information applies whether the problem is candida or some other bacteria.) Pay close attention to pH balance in the body.
Varicose veins	There are a number of key nutrients involved in supporting the heath of veins and arteries. Most important among them are vitamins C and E, bioflavonoids, and zinc. Studies have shown that a high fiber diet and regular exercise are also important to vein health. Extracts or syrups made from hawthorne berries, cherries, blueberries, and blackberries would contain a nice range of bioflavonoids. Grape seed extract is also excellent. People with varicose veins are not able to break down and utilize fibrin. This unprocessed fibrin is deposited just under the skin along the veins. Studies show that the presence of these hard lumps along large varicose veins indicates an increased risk of thrombophlebitis, myocardial infarction, pulmonary embolism, and stroke. Other herbs that may be helpful are: butcher's broom, cayenne (very important), dandelion root, garlic, gentian, gingko biloba, gotu kola, pleurisy root, and rosehips (for the vitamin C). Other helpful supplements include L-Carnitine, L-Arginine, and Bromelain.
Wounds	We have had a lot of success treating some pretty nasty wounds herbally—many of which *normal* people would have been sure required stitches. We have also treated really nasty wounds that did require stitches. For me the protocol is always pretty much the same. Treat the wound itself with yarrow essential oil. I prefer the dark blue one, but would use with confidence whatever I had. I have never seen infection in a wound that was treated with yarrow—the leaves, macerated and applied, in the wild are very effective. Yarrow has been known as "wound wort" for centuries for very good reasons. If the cut is fairly straight and you are not going for stitches, pull the edges together with lots of butterfly bandages. Wrap well and apply some cold to control the swelling that will otherwise tear out the bandaging. Wait a minimum of 48 hours, then unwrap carefully. If the wound has sealed, begin applying BHM salve to the area to prevent scarring and other problems. St. John's wort will heal and prevent nerve damage. Echinacea and gotu kola have shown excellent wound healing properties in clinical tests. The consistent application of BHM, and, later vitamin E oil will reduce any scarring which has occurred. Take lots of infection fighting herbs.

©**Copyright Butterfly Expressions, llc 2010   Butterfly Miracles with Herbal Remedies**

Latin Names of Some
Common Herbs

Alfalfa *Medicago sativa*

Angelica *Angelica archangelica*

Astragalus *Astragalus membranaceus*

Bayberry *Myrica cerifera*

Beet root *Beta vulgaris rubra*

Bilberry *Vaccinium myrtillus*

Black cohosh *Cimicifuga racemosa*

Black walnut *Juglans nigra*

Blessed thistle *Cnicus benedictus*

Blue cohosh *Caulophyllum thalictroides*

Blue vervain *Verbena hastata*

Brigham tea *Ephedra viridis*

Buchu *Agathosma betulina*

Buckthorn *Rhamnus frangula*

Burdock *Arctium lappa*

Butcher's broom *Ruscus aculeatus*

Calendula *Calendula officinalis*

Canada snake *Asarum canadense*

Cape aloes *Aloe ferox*

Cascara sagrada *Rhamnus purshiana*

Catnip *Nepeta cataria*

Cayenne *Capsicum annum*

Chamomile *Matricaria recutita*

Chapparal *Larrea tridentata*

Chaste tree *Vitex agnus castus*

Chickweed *Stellaria media*

Cinnamon *Cinnamomum cassia*

Cleavers *Galium aparine*

Cloves *Syzygium aromaticum*

Coltsfoot *Tussliago farfara*

Comfrey leaf *Symphytum officinale*

Comfrey root *Symphytum officinale*

Corn silk *Zea mays*

Cramp bark *Viburnum opulus*

Cranberries *Vaccinium oxycoccos*

Damiana *Turnera diffusa*

Dandelion *Tarazacum officinale*

Devil's claw *Harpagophytum procumbens*

Dong quai *Angelica sinensis*

Dulce *Rhodymenia palmetta*

Echinacea angustifolia *Echinacea angustifolia*

Echinacea purperea *Echinacea purpurea*

Elder berries *Sambucus nigra*

Elder flower *Sambucus nigra*

Elecampane *Inula helenium*

Eleuthero *Eleutherococcus senticosus*

Eyebright *Euphrasia officinalis*

False unicorn *Chamaelirium luteum*

Fennel *Roeniculum vulgare*

Fenugreek *Trigonella foenum graecum*

Gentian *Gentiana lutea*

Ginger *Zingiber officinale*

Ginkgo *Ginkgo biloba*

Ginseng panax *Panax quinquefolium*

Ginseng red *Panax quinquefolium*

Golden rod *Solidago virgaurea*

Goldenseal leaf *Hydrastis canadensis*

Goldenseal root *Hydrastis canadensis*

Gotu kola *Centella asiatica*

Gravel root *Eupatorium purpureum*

Hawthorne *Crataegus laevigata*

Hops *Humulus lupulus*

Horehound *Marrubium vulgare*

Horseradish *Armoracia rusticana*

Horsetail *Equisetum arvense*

Hydrangea *Hydrangea arborescens*

Hyssop *Hyssopus officinalis*

Juniper berries *Juniperus communis*

Kelp *Ascophyllum nodosum*

Lavender *Lavandula angustifolia*

Lemon balm *Melissa officinalis*

Licorice *Glycyrrhiza uralensis*

Lobelia *Lobelia inflata*

Lomatium *Lomatium dissectum*

Marshmallow *Althaea officinalis*

Milk thistle *Silybum marianum*

©Copyright Butterfly Expressions, llc 2010   **Butterfly Miracles with Herbal Remedies**

Mistletoe *Viscum album*

Motherwort *Leonurus cardiaca*

Mullein *Verbascum thapsus*

Myrrh *Commiphora molmol*

Nettles *Urtica dioica*

Oatstraw *Avena sativa*

Olive leaf *Olea europaea*

Oregano *Origanum vulgare*

Oregon grape *Mohonia aquifolium*

Osha *Ligusticum porteri*

Papaya *Carica papaya*

Parsley root *Petroselinum crispum*

Passion flower *Passiflora incarnata*

Pau d'arco *Tabebuia heptaphylla*

Peach tree *Prunus persica*

Peppermint *Mentha piperita*

Periwinkle *Vinca minor*

Plantain *Plantago major*

Pleurisy root *Asclepias tuberosa*

Poke root *Phytolacca americana*

Raspberry *Rubus idaeus*

Red clover *Trifolium pratense*

Red root *Ceanothus americanus*

Rehamania *Rehmannia glutinosa*

Rosehips *Rosa canina*

Rosemary *Rosmarinus officinalis*

Safflower *Carthamus tinctorius*

Sage *Salvia officinalis*

Sarsaparilla *Smilax medica*

Saw palmetto *Serenoa repens*

Senna *Senna alexandrina*

Sheep sorrel *Rumex acetosella*

Shepherd's purse *Capsella bursa pastoris*

Skullcap *Scutellaria lateriflora*

Slippery elm *Ulmus rubra*

Spikenard *Aralia racemosa*

Squawvine *Mitchella repens*

St. John's wort *Hypericum perforatum*

Stillingia *Stillingia sylvatica*

Stone root *Collinsonia canadensis*

Thimble berry *Rubus parviflorus*

Thyme *Thymus vulgaris*

Turkey rhubarb *Rheum palmatum*

Usnea *Usnea barbata*

Uva ursi *Arctostaphylos uva ursi*

Valerian *Valeriana wallichii*

Watercress *Nasturtium officinale*

White birch *Betula pubescens*

White oak *Quercus alba*

White pine *Pinus strobus*

White willow *Salix alba*

Wild lettuce *Lactuca quercina*

Wild yam *Dioscorea villosa*

Wood betony *Stachys officinales*

Wormwood *Artemisia absinthium*

Yarrow *Achillea millefolium*

Yellow dock *Rumex crispus*

Yerba mansa *Anemopsis californicum*

Yerba santa *Eriodictyon californicum*

Yucca *Yucca schidigera*

©Copyright Butterfly Expressions, llc 2010   Butterfly Miracles with Herbal Remedies

INDEX

About the Author:

LaRee Westover began studying and living natural medicine over 30 years ago. She has been using her extensive knowledge of plant families and their medicinal qualities in her synergistic blending of essential oils in the commercial arena for over 15 years. LaRee has lectured widely throughout the Intermountain West. She has been writing this book and others for years and they are based on years of work and personal experience.

Also by LaRee Westover

Butterfly Miracles with **Essential Oils**

This practical approach to the use of essential oils allows the novice to begin using them effectivly and advanced practitioner to gain insight into the world of essential oils.

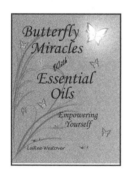

History of essential oils
Schools of thought
Tests and standards
Shelf life
Safety Guidelines
Pregnancy, childbirth , and children
Methods of use

Plant family and season
Meridians, chakras, and energy work
Descriptions of individual essential oils
Synergy and blended essential oils
Accomplishing goals with essential oils
Emotions and mood enhancement
Constituents

Coming Soon . . . . . .

Butterfly Miracles with **Homeopathic Remedies**

This book is a practical, in-depth look at homeopathic theory and types of remedies. It is meant to help the reader become proficient in the use of homeopathic remedies of all potencies.

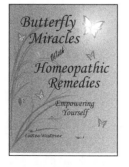

Basic Principles of Homeopathy
Types of Remedies
Dilution and Potency
How to Take Homeopathic Remedies
The Symptom Picture
Taking a Case History
Biochemic or Cell Salts

Flower Essence Remedies
Energetic Remedies
Remedies by Kingdom
   and Classification
Miasms
Suggestions for Specific Conditions
Suggestions for Epidemic Diseases